4-Cycle Karting Technology

By Bill Starrett

ISBN #0-936834-63-3

D1601970

Published By

STEVE SMITH
AUTOSPORTS
PUBLICATIONS

P. O. Box 11631 / Santa Ana, CA 92711 / (714) 639-7681

Manufactured and printed in USA

Table of Contents

About The Author

William E. (Bill) Starrett is a native Chicagoan, who has been involved in and around racing from a chain-drive midget, through many types and classes of racing machines, completing the full cycle with a chain-drive kart. His special love is midgets and sprints on dirt.

In 34 years with the Air Force, he spent his time in flying, engineering, aircraft modifications, computer specialties, and training others in each of these areas.

"Retired" since 1974, he is now an ordained Baptist pastor, serving the First Baptist Church of Fountain, Colorado.

Dedication

This book is dedicated to my wife Betty, whose love has supported and encouraged me for these 46 years; to our grandson Mike, whose short racing career was as outstanding as I wish mine could have been; and to those new racers who, I hope, will benefit from what these pages contain.

I would like to add a special thanks. It has been said that almost everything that anyone knows was learned from someone else. My greatest mentor was an unforgettable Professor of Logistical Analysis, who taught me to gather information from all possible sources, to seek the reasons for all things, and always to think for myself.

My thanks go to the numerous racers, builders, engineers and authors who have taken the time to explain "why" as well as "what." Without their willingness to present and explain their ideas, a book such as this could never have been written.

Bill Starrett

NOTICE

INTRODUCTION

This book was originally prepared for use as a series of texts, used to give a group of newcomers to "four cycle" kart racing a foundation for understanding in quite a number of important areas, both in karting and in other forms of racing.

It is not intended to be a step-by-step do it yourself set of directions on how to do specific jobs on a specific engine or chassis. Neither is it intended to explain how to buy a kart, register for a race meet, etc.

Herein are found many of the "little things", and the reasons for those practices, that most experienced racers have learned over a period of many years.

These discussions are centered about the 4-stroke engine, with little specifically associated with the 2-stroke classes. The reasons for this omission are:

1) It seems that most beginners start in the relatively slower, and less expensive, 4 strokes, rather than in the faster and more expensive 2 strokers.

2) 4-stroke engines seem to offer more opportunities for the new racer to experiment, and to learn some of the relationships between various areas in the mechanical aspects of racing vehicles.

3) Everything in this book, with the exception of references to valve trains, applies to both the 2-stroke and the 4-stroke engine/chassis combinations.

4) Finally, and perhaps most important, everything offered here (except chain and centrifugal clutch info) will apply directly to other types of racing vehicles that may be encountered.

You will find that racing in karting, Formula 1, Indy, NASCAR, etc., is a mass of compromises. For example a car cannot be geared for both acceleration and top speed. Setting up for easiest handling in left turns and right turns and straights is another example of compromising.

Karting is a family sport. Young boys and girls can learn from an early age mechanical and driving skills that will carry over to adult life. Karting develops the self discipline and self esteem necessary to the development of healthy and happy individuals.

Just remember that there are no real secrets in racing. The so called "secrets" are just things that others haven't heard about yet, or figured out for themselves.

Chapter 1

STARTING RACING

Nothing is more gratifying in amateur racing than to show up at a race track with a race-ready vehicle that can be taken out for a practice session, make a few adjustments, then qualify near the front. A kart that is race-readied on time will help the morale of the crew and the driver, and it will put that team on the officials' "good guys" list.

A race-ready kart will free up some time for socializing and helping others. This will contribute greatly to enjoying the sport in general, and to making the program a successful one. Certainly racing of any type involves repairing, tuning and adjusting, but a race-ready vehicle will be in the ballpark, and gear, pipe length and tire pressure changes will be kept to a minimum.

A systematic approach to maintenance and adjustment will prevent most of this ever happening. As an example, such an approach might include:

1) The use of a checklist for regular maintenance sessions between race meets. This will assure that no necessary items have been overlooked, and that the kart is ready when the driver registers for the next race.

2) Regular practice and test sessions at the local track, where both driving techniques and mechanical adjustments may be evaluated against the stopwatch.

3) Records of each test/practice session, and of each change made during a race meet, which will prevent confusion as to which change had what results.

These road racing "lay downs" reach speeds of up to 120 MPH. They are not recommended for beginners.

Keep detailed records of set ups that work best at the different tracks that you use. Delays will be prevented if the proper settings for tire pressures, toe, stagger, gears, carburetor jet, etc., have been determined and set.

Finally, while not all of the following subjects will apply to the beginning classes, they should be well understood as the driver plans to move up in class.

Gearbox karts are a lot of fun. Note the shifter by the steering wheel and the large K & N air filter.

Courteous drivers let other guys go by when they know they are getting in the way. Always raise your hand when the race is over or when going into the pits.

Welcome To Karting Terminology

When a newcomer arrives in karting with some knowledge of other forms of racing, he will often hear someone make statements that seem to be vague, or outright contradictory. Karting has its own language, just as businesses and sports each have theirs. For example, in almost all of American auto racing a "sprint" is raced on dirt, 1/4 to 1 mile ovals. In karting, a "sprint" is raced on paved short tracks, having both right and left turns. A "speedway" is a very short, dirt oval in karting. "Fuel" is a word that does not just refer to whatever liquid is burned in an engine. In some cases "fuel" is illegal in any engine, in other cases the word refers to racing gasoline. In still others it concerns methanol, and in yet others it deals with methanol that contains additives.

An "event" in Karting is not an individual race, but the entire group of races that are conducted in a single time period on a single track. Thus eight or ten races, held over a two day period, could be called an event.

An apparently contradictory term is "main event". The "main", or "main event", is not the climax, or most important race in an event, with the winner recognized as the top driver of the day. It is simply the last race in the event, and carries no more points or credit than any of the other heats. In other words, the main event is really the last heat of the event. It may be a little longer than the others, but it is of no greater importance than any of the other heats.

Perhaps the most confusing, even as one moves from one karting association to another, is the use of the word "stock". There is talk of stock engines, box stock, as delivered stock, manufacturer's stock, modified stock, limited modified stock, open stock, etc.

A "stock" kart engine bears no more resemblance to what a manufacturer would ship, than a NASCAR "stock car" resembles what could be bought in a car dealer's showroom.

This is not intended to ridicule, or in any way put down karting. The above examples are listed to emphasize the need to study the association rule book and to question any rule that are not understood.

Talk with the head tech inspector in your association. Do not just ask some other driver — he might be as confused as you are.

Think For Yourself

Many karters will routinely ask others what they should do, when matters are not going as they expect them to. By this they are usually wanting to be told what tire pressures, gears, plugs, jets, etc., they should be using.

If they would just think this through, they would realize that what they are asking is among the best ways to guarantee that they will never learn what to do, when to do it, and why it should be done.

No two kart/engine/driver combinations are alike. No two drivers weigh exactly the same, have exactly the same chassis design, exactly the same chassis flexibility, exactly the same engine, and exactly the same driving skill and technique. Also, many of the theories that are used by many in karting are nothing more than "old wive's tales". Ideas that have no standing in technical or mechanical fact are as popular (and incorrect) as the old idea that huge tail fins would make the family car more stable on the highway.

For example, for many months theoretical ideas concerning certain engine/kart modifications were discussed openly, and almost without exception being ridiculed by some of the "old hands" in karting. Yet, two karts each took the championship in their class, between them taking advantage of seventeen of those ideas that "we tried it and it won't work."

So much for letting someone else decide what combinations are best. Remember too that the other guys on the track are all your competitors and you may pose a threat to them.

The great Wilbur Shaw said that the secret to successful racing was to learn to "think like an engine". Mark Donohue, in his book "The Unfair Advantage", shows that the secret lies in preparation, imagination, and skillful driving.

Yet, there are still many who want others to do their thinking for them, and who explode in a flurry of fixing "things that ain't broke", copying what they think others have done with no logical plan of action in mind and then they wonder why the results are not what they had hoped for. Think for yourself.

Racing in the dirt requires special preparation to prevent mud from sticking to the kart. The number panels should be sprayed with WD-40 to prevent mud from sticking, so the scorers can see the numbers.

Test and Practice

In professional racing it is a way of life for the teams to test their cars for months before the start of each season, and for days or even weeks before an individual race. If these people are willing to spend many thousands of dollars doing this, there seems to be a serious message for the amateur.

Testing and practicing are not just a time to have some fun. This is where you can find out for yourself the various ideas and adjustments that work, or that do not work, for your particular situation.

Each practice session should be a time to learn something new about the kart, the driver, and the track, but never more than one thing should be changed at one time. If, for

Here is a typical example of why it is important to stay low in the turns on an oval track. A kart has spun in front of 126 and he can now overtake the spun kart on the inside. The kart behind him is too high and he will have to go around the incident on the outside in the loose dirt.

example, the tire pressures or the carburetor jet has been changed, and also the driver has tried several different lines through the corners, how can you tell which one brought about any lap time change that you might have noticed?

Each mechanical change, and each alternate line through each corner, should be tested for 8 to 20 laps. The last four laps should be timed for an average. This way will bear positive knowledge of what each change does to lap times.

Also, be sure to keep those detailed records. In time, after a number of such controlled test sessions, you will find that you can decide whether to change spark plugs, gear ratios, tire pressures, etc., without having to carefully reason the solution to your particular program. A notebook, pencil and a stopwatch are probably the most important and least expensive tools for racers.

It might appear very macho to make changes based on a hunch, or on what someone else is doing, but one will invariably find that the consistently front running racers in any type of racing will be the ones that are prepared systematically.

Comfort and Control

One thing that should always be kept in mind, when operating any vehicle, is the fact that a driver cannot drive to his full capability if his mind and body are involved in keeping his body in the seat, getting a grip on the steering wheel or stretching his legs towards the pedals.

Professional racing teams go to great extents having seats built to fit each driver, and placing the seat, wheel, and pedals so that the driver can give his complete attention to driving, and they use 5 or 6 point belts!

The nonchalant driver who drapes one wrist across the top of the wheel, slouches with his arm along the seat back,

These Kali karts come with nice mounts and foot rests. These foot rests can be used on other karts as well. Note the simple way the throttle cable is installed.

Pedals can be easily repositioned for small drivers. The rods can be cut and threaded. Pedal mounts can be purchased from K & P Manufacturing or they can be fabricated out of square tubing.

or drives as if trying to hold the roof in place, is in no position to take immediate action if a tire blows, he hits a pothole, or someone hits him.

Neither is the "little old lady" (of either sex) who leans forward and hugs the wheel, because she realizes what a death-defying act it is to drive a car in traffic.

In most types of motor racing the cars are stiffly suspended (karts have no suspension) which causes them to bounce and jump around the track. Karts hit berms and hay bales or tires, and taking reverse cambered turns tries to throw the driver out of the kart, all the while having other karts coming into sudden contact. Combinations of these things will happen dozens of times in every race. The time to prepare to combat them is at the shop by keeping the driver secure and comfortable.

Adjusting the Seat

Start with adjusting the seat for comfort and endurance. When first getting a kart, climb aboard, lean back in the seat, place your hands in your lap, and relax. The basic body position should be comfortable enough to remain seated for 20 to 30 minutes without moving, yet you should feel snugness around your hips and ribs. The snugger the better — you should feel as though you have to squeeze yourself into the seat.

If your seat does not fit you this closely, add padding where necessary. Once you get the proper fit, cement the padding into place so that it will not slip. Remember that this keeps you in place — as belts would under other conditions.

Now move your legs out to the pedals. The backs of your legs should just touch the front edge of the seat, without any noticeable pressure, while your feet operate both

The padding in this seat looks very comfortable. Notice the radiator and the braided water line going into the head. These braided lines should be used exclusively on all water cooled motors. A broken hose could severely burn the driver or a bystander.

pedals by ankle movement only. You should not have to bend your knees uncomfortably, or stretch at all, to work the pedals.

Now adjust the seat and/or the pedals so that you have complete control, while your body is relaxed and securely held in place.

If a fairing is used, check for clearance between it and the driver's legs. Basketball type elbow pads on the legs keep the fairing from rubbing off some skin.

Steering Wheel Adjustment

Next, adjust the steering wheel. There are several different ideas as to how the arms should be positioned, but stop to analyze the situation.

In Formula cars the "arms-out position" is necessary, because there is no room for elbow movement in those narrow cockpits. In all other forms of racing, notice that this position is not used.

Many studies have been made, both of driving, and the muscular actions used in driving, and they all have come to the same conclusion. For best control under all conditions, your steering action should be a swinging movement in the upper arms and shoulders.

Kart steering wheels have limited adjustability. The upper steering shaft mounts usually have three holes for up and down adjustment. The steering shaft length is set but it can be changed by purchasing a new shaft or cutting and welding the old one (make sure only a certified welder does any welding on your steering parts). The hands should be about 1 to 2 inches below the shoulder height while sitting in the kart. Move the steering wheel up or down to get the best possible adjustment.

Most karts use this method for adjusting the steering wheel height. The safety wire on the steering wheel bolts is required by IKF and WKA on all critical fasteners. Lock nuts are added safety.

Finally, with everything adjusted to fit the body, check the stability of the feet. The floorpan may need to be built up or use heel cups. With the kart set up in this manner, it becomes an extension of the body. This allows the driver to use his mental and physical abilities to race, instead of spending half his time just hanging on.

Competition Driving

Practically all of us firmly believe that we are just about the finest, and the most skillful, driver that ever sat behind a steering wheel. However, the more we get into any form of racing, and the more we compare our driving with other racers, the more many of us realize that we will never know everything.

Even highly experienced race drivers — winners in midgets, sprints, stocks, and sports cars — have spun out regularly, flipped, or continually bumped into others during their early attempts to drive a racing kart at speed.

The first thing that should be realized is that races are not necessarily won by the driver with the fastest vehicle, the heaviest foot, or the most bravery. Driving technique, being properly set up for the next corner, and moving through traffic, require much experience and are the keys to winning.

There are very few places on most tracks where absolute top speed is obtainable. Getting around the corners, being properly set up before entering the corner, the ability to "read" the track, traffic, and other drivers, are all vitally important.

"Walking the track" is a technique that has proven to be of utmost value. Either physically walk the entire track — in reverse (against traffic) — or stand in a place where the entire course can be studied. For example; if turn #4 leads into the fastest part of the course, you will want to exit that corner as fast as possible. The entry to the turn should be decided to determine the most advantageous exit.

This will automatically force you to consider where you should have exited and entered turn #3 and turn #2, etc.

Always keep in mind that the key to successful racing lies in your head not in how far you can push a pedal, or how brave you are. A really good driver usually does not look as though he is going as fast as he is actually moving. His smoothness, ability to look ahead and decide what the situation will be in the next few seconds, and his knowledge of where he should be on the track at that particular moment, all make it appear as though he is not trying as hard as the other drivers.

The smoother the driver becomes, in steering, accelerating, turning, and braking, the faster his lap times will become. It will also result in being recognized as a skillful driver who can be trusted in close, fast moving traffic.

The good driver is aware of the traffic behind him. Few drivers are more dangerous than the one who sticks his chin on the steering wheel and stares straight ahead like a horse wearing blinders.

On most tracks there are sharp or hairpin turns where the wise driver will glance over his shoulder (or across the track) to see what traffic is developing behind him. This is not only common courtesy, but it makes good driving sense. Many drivers have been hit from behind, spun out, or wrecked, because they drifted or swerved into the path of a racer that they didn't even know was in back of them.

In every racing organization each driver is required and expected to give way to another driver who is obviously faster than himself. This does not mean that he should give

Esses should be taken with the last turn in mind. The line through each turn is compromised to maximize the last turn into the straightaway.

The approach to a turn is the most important part of the turn. Braking should be done smoothly and the turn must be entered with the exit in mind.

This kart entered the turn too late. This will cause it to exit late and to push in the corner.

This kart has entered the turn too early. It will come out early and slowly.

way to everyone, but if the move-over flag is waved, he must allow the faster, or lapping, karts to pass.

Probably the best experience that the new driver can get is to watch the consistent front runners. Following the more experienced drivers around the track in practice, or standing at various locations to watch them carefully, will allow the observer to determine the lines, braking points and the time when the throttle is picked back up. See where they accelerate or brake (watch their feet on the pedals), their usual lines through different corners, and the relaxed way that they "ease" their karts around the track. Then spend some time practicing what was observed. As you become more comfortable with the kart at full power, try varying lines through each corner deliberately going into the corner "too high" or "too low". In a race, with other karts around, it will not always be easy to drive the ideal line.

A famous driver once said that he won more races in the grandstands than he did on the track. By that he meant when he was not in actual competition, whether practicing or just watching others drive, he carefully studied the habits of his competition. For example, one driver may usually drift outward on a certain corner. Another may usually brake too early or too late. Still another might hug the inside line, or yank his kart around the turns.

This knowledge can be used to "set up" another driver, and to get past him when he least expects it, or when he

Notice how tight national champion Richie Hearn is keeping the right front wheel to the curb. The driver must take advantage of the whole width of the track. Running over this type of curbing upsets the chassis. Accurate driving like this earned Richie two Duffies driving for Manning Karting.

Racing in a tight pack with other drivers that can be trusted is greatly exhilarating. Most dirt tracks offer only one groove. Number 154 is out of the line and he is going to lose out to 159. By the way, try to keep the numbers to single or double digits to make the scorer's job easier.

that they cannot win races by skillful and thoughtful driving.

Open wheel racing is basically dangerous, whether driving a kart, a sprinter, or an Indy car. Without several hundred pounds of fenders and roll cage for protection, kart drivers are largely at the mercy of each other. Sooner or later, the "slam-bang artist" or "hero driver" will find that someone will toss him on his head, smash his engine, or run him into a wall — always "accidentally", of course.

Among the greatest pleasures in any form of racing is running lap after lap, fighting for the lead against drivers whose techniques, skills, and judgements have earned the trust of other drivers and who trust the others in the very same way.

One final thought about driving: a multiple USAC champion driver, talking about another world recognized driver, said: "He learned to go fast before he learned to drive." Think about it.

(Left) This kart is far off the line to the outside. This driver entered the turn too late or too late or too fast.

(Below) Number 4 is set to enter the turn. 98 is too far in and he is not using the whole track. 98 is using the passing line, but he is too far back to attempt a pass.

thinks he has the other driver blocked. These "machos" are the ones that cannot be trusted in close traffic — but they also are the ones who often can be set up for a pass.

Some drivers seem to believe that they are showing great skill and bravery by making sudden movements, "bulling" their way past others, and by cutting off those who are trying to pass them. Actually these drivers are showing that they are mediocre and dangerous, and

These two karts are displaying good lines, in and out of the turns.

Definitions

Before continuing, here are the meanings of several standard racing words and terms, some of which will be used in the following pages:

BLUBBER (BOBBLE): This is the "bubbling" sound that is heard instead of the normal sharp and crisp sound. It usually appears when standing on the throttle in a turn, or when coming out of a turn.

CUT CLEAN: This is a technique that allows the spark plug to be used as an indicator of actual combustion in the engine. After warming the engine completely, and taking several laps at high speed, with full load, the throttle is held wide open while the ignition is cut off, and the vehicle allowed to coast to a stop.

DIAL IN: This is a general term, applicable to the engine, carburetor, chassis, tire pressures, etc., and combinations of those items. Each adjustment is varied slowly and carefully, and tested under varying conditions, until the component or the combination of components function at their utmost capability.

FEATHERING: This is the technique where the throttle is eased on or off, providing reduced or increased power; but not full power or no power.

HOT (COLD) PLUG: These do not alter the temperature of the engine. The "hot" plug has a relatively long insulator, which retains heat, and causes the electrodes to run at a hotter temperature. The "cold" plug has a shorter insulator, which transfers heat more rapidly, causing the electrodes to run at colder temperatures.

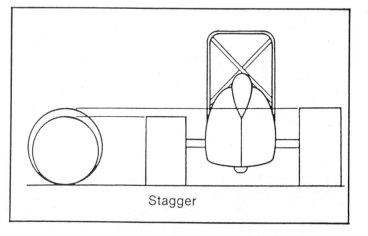

Stagger

LEAN (RICH) MIX: Internal combustion engines produce maximum power when run at a specific ratio of fuel to air of 12 to 1 in pounds of air to pounds of gasoline. Since this ratio is affected by temperature, barometric pressure and humidity, carburetors must be adjusted to get the best ratio. Too much fuel in the mix (rich) will cost power, foul plugs, clog valve ports, and build carbon. Too much air (lean) will overheat plugs and valves, and can destroy the engine by detonation.

LINE: The actual route that a race vehicle takes in going around a corner. It may be the fastest way around, or it may bring the car out of the corner in the best place on the track for the turn ahead.

STAGGER: This refers to the difference in circumference between two tires on the same axle. Most commonly on

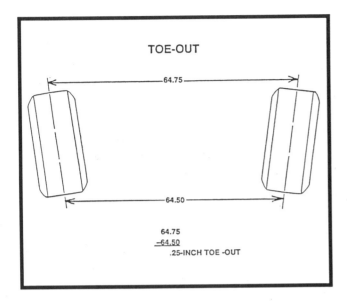

the rear axle, it is "positive" stagger if the right tire is larger in circumference than the left. Positive stagger is used on oval tracks, to facilitate turning left. Judicious use of a small amount of stagger on sprint and road racing karts can also yield some benefits.

STUMBLE: This is a feeling similar to the engine losing power for a second or two, as you suddenly open the throttle.

TOE IN (OUT): When the front centerline of the tires on one end of the vehicle (usually the front) are closer together than the rear centerlines of the same tires, this is called "toe in". The opposite, front farther apart than the rear, is called "toe out".

This kart is very loose either from chassis set-up or from driver error. This scrubs off a lot of speed right at the most critical part of the turn where power should be applied to carry the speed out of the turn into the straightaway.

A wet dirt track will be loose. The drier the track gets, the worse the kart will push (understeer). The mechanics should keep a sharp eye out for changing track conditions to tune the chassis and tires to the dirt. A loose kart can use a higher gear (smaller size) while a kart that pushes can use a lower one (larger number of teeth).

TRACK: This is the distance between the center lines of the front wheels (front track), or the centerlines of the rear wheels (rear track).

TRAILING THROTTLE: This is when you feather the throttle while gently applying the brakes. Most often used in a turbo powered vehicle to keep the turbo RPMs up, it can be used on a kart to get improved front wheel grip when entering a fast, sweeping turn.

OVER/UNDER STEER: Commonly called "loose", over-steer is the condition where the rear wheels begin to slide (in a turn) before the front wheels do. Called "pushing", understeer is the opposite of oversteer. Here the front tires lose their grip while the rear tires still have a good "bite" on the ground.

Tire Compounds

Each manufacturer makes tires having different blends of rubber, carbon, and other components. Some of these combinations will give long wear, others a better grip allowing faster cornering, and still others give variations between these objectives.

However, hard tires, having long wear characteristics, do not permit as fast cornering as the "soft" tires. At the same time, the soft tires will wear out much faster than the hard ones will.

Number 26 is out of the groove and spinning his wheels in the loose dirt. 126 is down low on hard dirt where the tires can get traction.

The novice kart driver would probably be smart to start out with hard rubber on all four wheels, thus permitting many hours of testing and practice at a fairly reasonable cost.

As he becomes more proficient he might decide to use a combination of soft tires on certain wheels, and hard tires on the others, or he may go for soft tires all around.

Having fun yet? You can get hurt without hitting anything while racing a kart. Look at the position of the driver's head. Thanks for neck braces.

But always remember the wear factor. Soft tires (especially on the front wheels) will wear out in 3 to 4 race meets, or equivalent practice. Hard rubber will last several times longer.

Another factor to consider in connection with selection and wear of tires, is the track that will be driven on. Comparing experience on a 1/4 mile sprint track incorporating 6 or 7 turns in both directions, with a mile or longer track of the same general layout, will show that tires last much longer on the longer track.

The longer track, with longer straights, allows the tires to cool more than the short track. On the shorter tracks the tires will build up to a higher temperature before stabilizing, which will result in more rapid wear.

Tire Pressures

In determining tire pressures, a basic objective is to use just enough air to have maximum contact across as much of the tread as possible, and to prevent the tire from rolling under while cornering.

A secondary rule for karts is to keep the front pressures about 10 to 20 percent lower than the rears. A good starting point for karts is 17 pounds in the front tires, and 20 pounds in the rears. Drive about 10 to 20 laps at speed, carefully noting how the kart handles. Then raise or lower the front pressures, one or two pounds apiece, and repeat the test drive of 10 to 20 laps.

Tires are the name of the game in any form of racing. Speedway requires many different types of tires to adapt to the changing track conditions.

Chapter 2

HANDLING ADJUSTMENTS

Selecting Gear Ratios

In selecting the gear ratios, it is best to start with the combination being used by the experienced drivers in the same class with the same engine that you are using. Then study the track that will be driven on, and select the fastest and the slowest places on that particular track.

For example, the end of the main straight might be the point of highest speed, and a particular turn might slow karts down more than any other place on the track.

Drive 5 to 10 laps at speed, paying particular attention to your actual speed and response at each of these two points. Then ask yourself some questions:

1) At the slowest point, does the engine take full power smoothly? If it stumbles, go to a one tooth larger gear on the rear axle. If it feels as though it still has some power to spare, go to a smaller axle gear.

When it comes to tires on karts, bigger is not always better. Bigger tires can "bog" a motor down. A change to a lower gear (larger number of teeth) would be in order. Notice the large amount of negative camber in the left front of the kart at right.

2) At the fastest point, does the engine seem to still be accelerating when you have to back off for the coming turn? Does it seem to "level off" just before you reach the back off point? Or does it run out of power well before you reach that back off point?

If you seem to still be accelerating just before you must back off, go one tooth larger on the axle gear. If you run out of power well before the turn, try one tooth smaller on the axle.

3) No track is perfect. Therefore the best gear combination will have to be a compromise between the fastest (high end) and the slowest (low end) power situations.

Once again, a study of the track will help make the final decision. If your particular track has more than one slow turn, you might want to sacrifice a little top end to get better pull out of the hole (better acceleration out of the turns).

If, on the other hand, there is only one slow turn, and more than one fast section, or a particularly long high speed section, you probably will decide to give up some of the low end in order to capitalize on top speed.

Weight Distribution

In most racing organizations, each class has definite minimum weight requirements. Many unaware drivers will simply add some ballast as required to reach the minimum to satisfy the rules.

Some will just "hang on" some weight, wherever it is most convenient, or where it seems to look the best. However, the placement of such ballast can have a dramatic effect on handling and lap times. Keep in mind that it is never advisable to add weight, above the legal minimum, to profit more from better handling than from absolute minimum weight. There are plenty of other ways to set the chassis.

Basic rules to keep in mind for adding ballast include:

1) Always bolt weights to the main chassis structure. Never use hose clamps, wire, or tape. Vibrations and hard bumps often break improperly installed ballast loose.

2) Weight added to the front end will reduce understeer. Weight added to the rear end will reduce oversteer.

18

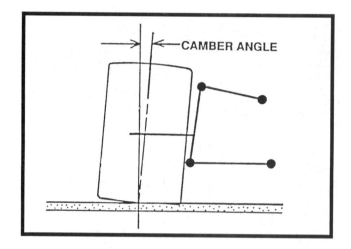

3) On an oval track, weight added to the inside (or left) side will increase cornering speed.

4) Never add more weight than is needed to meet minimum requirements. Move the seat and the lead around until you arrive at the desired handling.

5) A tire pyrometer such as the Digatron units sold by G.I.R.P. will be of great help in setting up the weight distribution. The Digatron G.I.R.P. pyrometers come with instructions. More information on tire temperatures and weight distribution can also be found in other Steve Smith Autosports books.

Obviously, the lighter the kart is to begin, the more you can shift ballast to where it does the most good. Fairings, wings, etc., may look good, but they cannot be moved to a more advantageous location.

Under most conditions, you should keep your total weight as close to the minimum as possible, However, some karts and some tracks require additional weight, which improves handling and cornering enough to more than make up for slightly decreased acceleration.

When adding permanent ballast to the front of a kart, here's a tip that will make it invisible. Remove the front bumper, drill small holes in the rear most portions of the bumper, and prop it up on its nose. Pour the needed amount of small lead shot into the holes while tapping the bumper to assure that the shot packs down toward the front of the tubing. Squirt waterproof glue into the holes to seal and immobilize the shot. Allow a couple of hours for the glue to set up before reinstalling the bumper.

Front End Alignment

One of the main reasons why one driver will consistently walk away from his competition, with apparently identical engines and experience, is the amount of time each one spends on the matter of how the "rubber meets the road". Any four-wheel vehicle's handling is heavily influenced by four front end alignment factors:

Caster: The amount that the steering pivot tilts toward the back of the vehicle, like the forks of a bicycle. This causes the vehicle to tend to move in a straight line. When the wheels are steered caster will generate camber in proportion to the amount of caster dialed in the front end.

Camber: The amount, and direction, that the front wheels tilt in or out at the top. This is used to cause the tire to be loaded at the center of the road contact area. Tires that tilt outward at the top are considered to have "positive" camber. Tires that tilt inward have "negative camber".

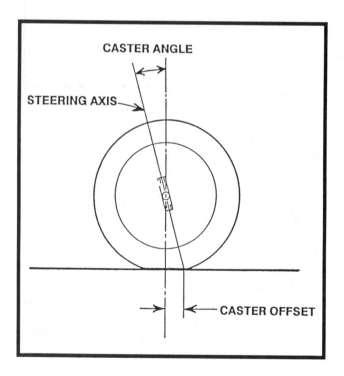

The hairpin clip on the spindle bolt makes for quick adjustment. The camber is adjustable via the offset bushing at the top of the spindle. The shims on the spindle shaft are used to offset the wheels.

This kart is suffering from excessive front wheel negative camber, as noted by the extreme inside tire wear.

Toe: As it is with a bicycle or motorcycle, tires always tend to turn in the direction that they are tipped. Thus wheels that are tipped outward (positive camber) will try to turn apart, wheels tipped inward (negative camber) tend to turn toward each other. Wheels that are tipped in the same direction as is done in oval track racing, will both pull in that direction. Toe is adjusted to compensate for the effects of the camber that exists, to allow the wheels to tend to roll straight forward rather than turning in or out.

Ackermann: In a turn the inside wheel follows a smaller circle than the outside, so it must be turned (steered) a greater amount than the outer one. Many alignment people call this "toe out on turns".

Ackermann and caster settings are not critical to the beginning karter. A few karts have limited adjustments for caster and camber, but most have the adjustments "welded in".

The problem in a racing vehicle is that the camber/toe combinations resist each other in straight running, but when the wheels hit a small irregularity on the track surface the tire with the best traction tends to turn the vehicle toward itself. This is commonly called "wandering". Extreme stagger can also cause this on a wet dirt track as the rear wheels fight to gain traction.

On the other hand, if the front end seems to jump suddenly as you enter a turn, or make steering corrections in the straight, this can be caused by not enough toe in, too much toe out, or a bent frame. This is usually called "darting".

Checking the wear on the front tires of race cars might show signs of positive or negative camber. If the wear appears on the inside portion of the tire, it has excessive negative camber. If the wear is on the outside portion, the camber is too much to the positive. Furthermore, a kart that understeers will probably show some extra wear on

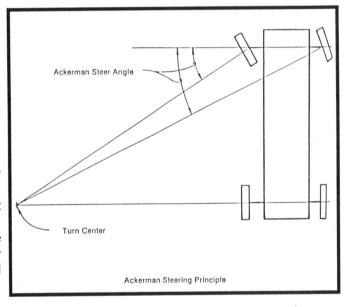

Ackerman Steer Angle

Turn Center

Ackerman Steering Principle

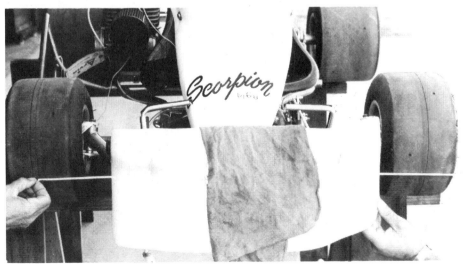

Measuring the front toe-out. Notice the thin lines on the tires from which the measurements are taken.

Kali karts feature adjustable camber and caster via this plate with three allen bolts. Note the fine workmanship on the spindle and tie rod.

Leaving a nut loose on each tie rod will prevent them from possibly bending or locking in place. The threads are strong enough and they will not pull out. Not all karts have this problem.

the inside of the front tires. This is caused by the driver turning the wheel more into the turns to compensate for the push, causing camber to build up from the caster.

You can check your kart by looking at the tires, or with a small level. Place the kart on a level piece of pavement, and have the driver or someone about his weight sit in the seat while a level is pressed against the outer side of the wheel rims. The level will indicate whether "positive" or "negative" camber exists. The amount of camber at rest is only a reference point as it will change due to chassis flex and caster. A graduated level can also be used to indicate the exact amount of camber. This should be checked after every race.

Most race cars that are set up for both left and right turns have negative camber. This is desired so that the outside tire will ride flat on the ground while the car negotiates the turns. Many vehicles that are driven on oval tracks will have negative camber on the right (outside) tire, and positive camber on the left (inside) wheel. Cars running radial tires require large amounts of camber to generate the desired tire slip angles.

The correct amount of camber can be arrived at with the use of a tire pyrometer and a skid pad. With correct toe adjustment for your kart, the handling will be more precise, there will be little or no darting or wander, the tires will scrub less and run cooler, and there will be less "rolling resistance" to eat up power. The tires will also last longer.

To set the toe properly, first locate an accurate tire centerline. Do not use tread marks, mold flashing, or sidewalls as these vary too much to be trusted.

Put the front end of the kart on a box, then with a pencil or scribe held steadily against a solid object, spin the wheel as you press the marker against the center of the tread. This will give an accurate measuring line. Another way is to wrap a length of masking tape around the tread, and use a ball point pen to make a very narrow, and very obvious, mark.

With both wheels marked, put the kart back on the ground, and have someone of about the driver's weight sit in the seat. Center the steering wheel, and be sure the arm from the shaft to the tie rods is perfectly vertical.

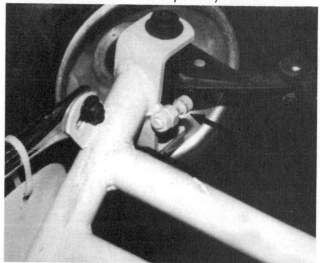

It is important to set the steering stop to prevent the steering from locking in place if it is turned too far.

Some karts come with adjustable spindles. These are nice for setting the corner weights and especially for changing the handling in the dirt.

Loosen, and adjust, each tie rod end so that each wheel points as straight ahead as possible. Reinstall, and tighten, the tie rod ends.

Now, measure the distances between the front marks and the rear marks on the measuring lines. Be accurate, to within 1/16-inch. Lengthen or shorten the tie rod (both, if yours is in two sections) until the desired toe (in or out) is set at 1/8-inch.

Test drive the kart, looking for darting, wander, handling on straights, and handling in turns. As was done when establishing the best tire pressures (see "Tires"), make small "plus and minus" toe adjustments (about 1/16-inch at a time), and retest, until you find the correct toe. Record this final figure for future use. It's easy to forget.

One other thing regarding the front end. If you have a slight encounter that results in a spindle steering arm being bent, do not pry it straight. This will probably change the Ackerman that has been designed into the chassis.

Instead, remove both wheels and spindles. Bolt the spindles together, top to top or bottom to bottom. Use a bolt the same diameter as the spindle pivot bolt used on your kart (it'll probably have to be longer than the two you have). Align the axles with each other, perfectly. Then have the damaged arm repaired or straightened, so that it too lines up correctly.

Adjusting Oversteer and Understeer

Due to the high percentage of weight on their rear wheels and because of the locked rear axle, most karts seem to understeer (push) most of the time. The following are some

Kart #159 is pushing (understeering) while the one at the left is loose (oversteering).

Front brake setup on a shifter kart. Offsetting the wheel this far from the spindle creates a large amount of scrub radius. Widening the front track will also create a tendency toward understeer.

A soft frame will cause the inside front wheel to get off the ground. These frames are well suited to dirt racing when the track is wet. The handling will probably go away when the track dries.

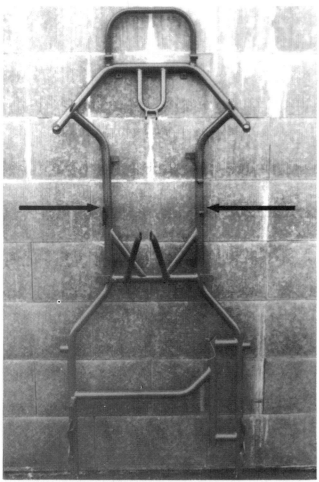

Kart frames are about as basic a structure as can be designed for racing. The flexibility is determined by the width of the waist, the size and thickness of the tubing and the length of the two tubes comprising the waist. The waist is the rectangular area located between the two steering mounts. This chassis has two triangulating bars at the rear of the waist to stiffen the chassis.

of the actions that can be taken to reduce understeer. Note that taking the opposite actions will reduce oversteer:

1) Narrow the front track, or widen the rear track.

2) Widen the front rims, or narrow the rear rims. However, the widest rims possible should be used to optimize handling.

3) Reduce toe in, or increase toe out (whichever the kart uses).

4) Add weight, or move ballast, forward.

5) Increase chassis flexibility forward of the driver's seat.

The trend for all types of racing cars is towards a wider front end and narrower rear end track. This will make a kart push even more, but note that the karts built this way also run more front end weight. Remember the old racing

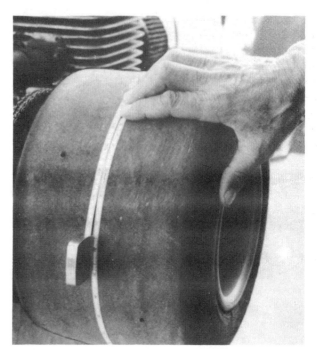

Correct method of measuring stagger. Use a thin, narrow tape and make sure it is flat against the tire.

adage: "A car that handles best in the turns will usually turn faster laps than a car that is faster on the straight."

Using Stagger

Stagger is simply the difference in circumference between two tires on one axle. It should be measured with a thin, narrow, tape measure, wrapped tightly around the tire surfaces. Use a thin tape — a wide or thick one gives a series of straight segments, and is not accurate enough.

To be certain that your measurement is as accurate as possible, "rock" the tire back and forth two or three times, using the tape like a drive belt. This will automatically line up the tape, avoiding a diagonal measurement.

To reduce existing stagger, should you want to do so, the following will often work:

Inflate the smaller tire to about 45 to 50 psi. Place the tire in direct sunlight for 2 to 3 hours, turning it occasionally to allow the sun to heat it as evenly as possible. This will soften the plies, and allow the tire to stretch. Cool the tire quickly by placing it in a large pan of cold water, or rinsing it with a hose. Deflate the tire to normal running pressure, and re-check the circumference.

You can make productive use of stagger, in either (or both) the front or rear, depending on your chassis and the handling effect that you want. Stagger is seldom used on karts that turn right and left because when the brakes are applied the kart with stagger tends to pull towards the smaller wheel. This is beneficial on oval tracks, but it is detrimental to a sprint kart trying to turn into a turn of the opposite direction that the stagger is set up for.

In the front, stagger can produce the same effect as "wedge" in a full sized racer. Imagine the smaller tire on the left front of the axle. This would cause the chassis to shift, taking a large amount of weight off that left front, and a smaller amount off the right rear. These weights would be shifted to the right front and left rear. However a large difference in tire size must be used to influence wedge to an appreciable point. Inflating the right front tire to stretch the tire would cause a loss of traction at that corner, causing the driver to think that the operation was successful at the detriment of optimum cornering force.

Front wedge is also used on oval track cars to cause the car to dive in the turn when the brakes are applied. If the inside tire diameter is smaller than the right, it will receive more torque from the brakes, thus pulling the front of the car into the turn. Naturally, a smaller tire on the right front would have the opposite effect. This will not work on karts since most do not have front brakes.

Stagger in the rear is much more important to handling than stagger in the front. The reason is the "locked" rear end, where each rear tire rotates exactly the same amount as the other, whether going straight or turning. Because of this, rear stagger may be used to make the kart tend to turn toward the smaller tire.

This kart is loose (understeering). Lowering the right spindle and/or raising the left would probably correct the situation — until the track dries. Taking out some stagger would also help.

This kart is pushing (understeering). Lowering the left spindle and/or raising the right would help. Increasing stagger would also reduce understeer, but go easy on the stagger.

The double axle mount helps reduce axle flex in the turns and it minimizes wear of the inside of the rear tires.

This kart is neutral handling. It is in a perfect four-wheel drift and the driver can use full throttle early, and he can control the kart with slight steering corrections.

There are two distinct advantages to using stagger — speed through the turn, and acceleration out of the turn.

With proper stagger (rear), the tendency of your kart will be to turn every time you apply power. This, of course, means that you can take turns in that particular direction faster than you could without stagger.

Remember that many passes originate in the ability of one racer to accelerate off the turns better than the one being passed. With proper stagger, and the resulting greater speed through the turn, you will naturally have a jump on others in the acceleration department.

Also, getting off the corners quicker helps to carry more speed down the straights. This is much more helpful than the small amount that might be lost by "dragging" one tire on the straight parts of the course.

Some people are afraid of stagger, understanding that while it might help in the turns, it offers more rolling resistance on the straights. However, they should remember that racing set ups are all a series of small compromises: tire pressures, gear ratios, weight locations, etc. The wise driver will set his kart up for the particular track that he is getting ready to race on instead of arriving at one set up, and doing nothing except changing gears when he goes from one track to another.

Study the track that you are setting up to run. Is there more footage in right turns, in left turns, or on the straights? Are there more right or left turn exits, and what does each lead into? Then decide on what front and/or rear stagger will help the most.

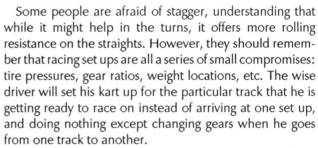

These kart stands can be made very inexpensively. They make transporting the kart easy, and help keep rocks and metal objects out of the tires.

This club has a nice scale set-up. The weigh-in procedure takes place after each qualifying session and after each race. Some clubs use grain scales that require lifting the kart on the platform.

Choose the fairings judiciously. Some can get hooked on other kart's bumpers while others can slide under the rear of other karts.

Chapter 3

FUEL SYSTEMS

When thinking in terms of getting fuel into a carburetted engine, you should think along the lines of "the more the better". Here we are not talking about the fuel/air mixture, but simply the availability of fuel to enter the carburetor at the end of a long, fast, possibly uphill, straightaway.

Remember that these little kart engines are running about 1 to 2 times the RPM that the manufacturer intended. This can create a number of situations where the engine is using more fuel than the original fuel system was designed to put into the float chamber. This, of course, would make the engine run on a very lean mixture, or even cause it to "cut out" for a few seconds (until the fuel pump could catch up).

Also, while most auto fuel pumps put out about 5 to 8 pounds of pressure, the little vacuum operated kart pumps only supply 1/2 pound! Whether you use Walbro, Mikuni or the Briggs pump in the carburetor, 1, 2, or 3 pumps, in series or in parallel, they can only produce the pressure and volume that the diaphragm spring and engine pulsations develop.

Add to that the fact that the longer the fuel line is, the greater the loss of volume, or strength of pressure waves, at the end of that line.

Another item that should be avoided is 90-degree bends. A sharp corner (a "T" or an "L") can lower pressure as much as 10 percent. If you must turn 90 degrees in close quarters, use two 45-degree fittings or a radiused piece of tubing.

Mount the fuel pump (or pumps) as close to the carburetor as possible. On a 2-stroke, one could mount the pump in any attitude that he desires, but on a 4 stroke the position is critical.

Because a 4-stroke crankcase is filled with circulating droplets of oil, and the pump gets its pulsations from the crankcase, these small drops of oil tend to get into the line, and work their way into the pump. This not only causes a mess when the oil eventually comes out the pump vent, but it decreases the movement of the diaphragm, thus decreasing the capacity of the pump.

The manufacturers recommend that on a 4-stroke engine, the pump should be mounted with the pulsation line

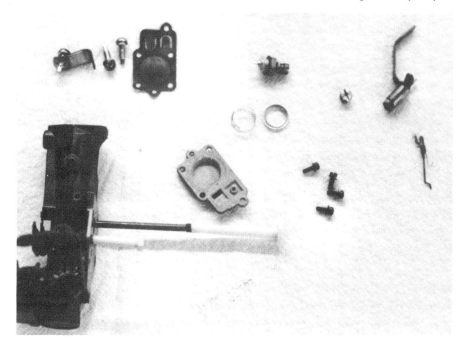

The carburetor on the Briggs is very simple. Use care not to damage the fuel pick up tubes. They are not repairable. The long pick up works with the pump to transfer the fuel to the small bowl in the tank for the shorter pick up. The short pick up actually feeds the engine via the vacuum in the carburetor throat.

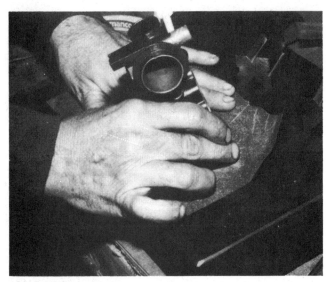

The carburetor gasket area is being surfaced on some wet and dry sandpaper that was dipped in solvent.

hanging straight down, toward the engine crankcase fitting. This will allow most (if not all) of the oil to drain back into the engine, instead of having it build up in the pump.

Some karters have gotten away from the oiling problem by tapping the pulsation line into the intake port, instead of into the crankcase. This works fine, so far as the oil problem is concerned. However it can cause a more serious problem. Since the intake port pulsations occur once every two revolutions (during the intake stroke) and the crankcase pulses occur once every revolution (as the

Proper venting of the fuel tank is very important. If air cannot take the place of the fuel that is being used by the engine, the pump will not be able to do its work. A filter at the breather will help keep the fuel clean.

piston moves up and down), you can see that the intake connected pump will only act half as often as the crankcase connected one, and therefore will only pump half as much fuel (on a 4-cycle engine).

Fuel Filtering

Filter the fuel as soon as possible after it leaves the tank. Keep the filter clean and check it at least every other race meet. It might sound very basic, but a lot of racers never bother to install or check a filter. Every particle of dirt that gets into the carburetor hurries the need for carb cleaning, and every particle that gets stopped by a filter reduces the amount of fuel available to the pump.

If methanol is used for fuel, do not use a paper fuel filter. Get one with a brass or plastic filtering element, either screen or porous. Water in the fuel (one of the problems with alcohol fuel) will cause a paper filter to swell and block the flow. Also, methanol often dissolves the glue on the end caps, causing the filter to separate. A clear filter, such as the K&N, will allow you to check its condition without disassembling it.

K&N filters can be used with any fuel and they are readily available at most kart and motorcycle shops.

Install a small piece of sponge over the breather of your fuel tank. If you use a small breather hose for the tank, install a K&N fuel filter. This will filter the air entering the tank as the fuel level diminishes.

Air Filters

Do not just get any kind of air filter and expect top performance. The filter should be matched to the driving conditions and engine, and it should be the pleated gauze type like the K&Ns. These filters need to be sprayed with oil to filter efficiently.

Always remember that while the sponge type filters offers very good filtration, it not only requires more filter area (larger unit), but demands more frequent and careful cleaning. Gauze type filters such as the K&Ns, are less air flow restrictive than any other filter.

Look in the K&N literature for formulas to calculate the correct size filter.

Setting The Butterfly

Remove the air cleaner, have someone hold the throttle wide open, and check the throttle butterfly position. It should be perfectly aligned with the gas flow through the venturi. The throttle stop on the outside of the carburetor alignment should not be relied upon for this alignment. Measurements have shown that factory assembly tolerances have about 1 out of 4 carburetors opening either a little too much, or not quite enough, when the pedal is pushed

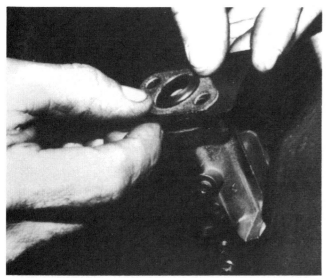

Junior classes use a restrictor plate between the engine and the carburetor. This requires the use of two more gaskets.

Spacer to be installed behind tank brace mount. This spacer is important on junior motors to make up for the extra thickness of the gaskets and the restrictor plate.

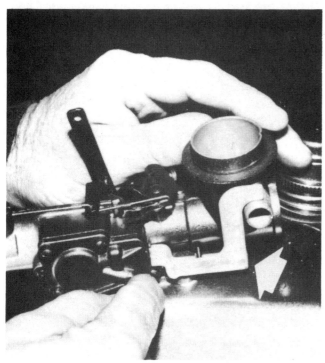

The carb saver is used to prevent breakage of the carburetor where it mounts to the tank.

The carburetor mounting bolts should be replaced with allen head bolts. They can be tightened down harder than the hex head bolts, and they are easier to reach with an angle allen wrench.

The top carburetor screw can be removed with a large screwdriver. The lower is more easily removed with a 3/8-inch wrench. Replace the screws with allen head bolts. They are stronger and more easily reached. Save the governor spring for a carburetor return spring.

Before installing the sheetmetal cover, drill a small hole in the tin as shown here. This will make an ideal location for the carb return spring.

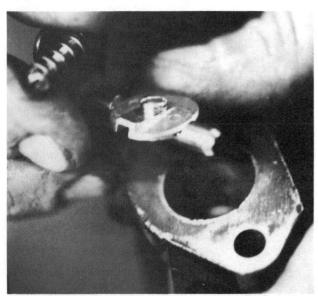

The butterfly mounts on top of the shaft. The screw should be installed with a dab of Loctite.

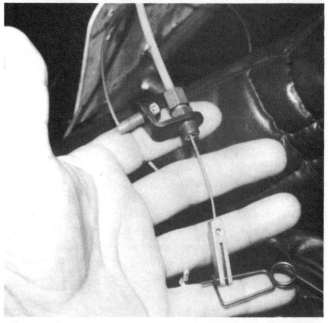

Nice throttle setup. Note the hairpin clip for easy removal.

to the floor. This has an effect similar to putting a block of wood under the throttle pedal.

Support your throttle cable about every 10 to 12 inches. The flex that comes in an unsupported cable will alter your sensitive throttle control and feel.

Always double check the throttle opening at the track. The throttle cable may have been set correctly at home, but variations in temperature will cause it to stretch or contract, changing the opening of the butterfly or stretching the cable.

Selecting A Gasoline

Many beginning (or novice) classes require the use of service station pump gasoline. "Higher" classes, and some organizations, permit other fuels.

Probably the most widely misused and misunderstood term regarding gasoline is "octane". The octane rating (not amount) of a fuel is simply the percentage of a test fluid (iso-octane) in a mixture with another fluid (N-heptane), which would give the same anti knock effect as the particular fuel being tested.

Notice that this is not a measure of the energy or power, or of the mileage that the fuel should provide. All gasolines have about the same energy content (19,000 to 19,500 BTUs per pound).

The higher octane (performance or research) number fuel has just been blended to permit detonation free operation in an engine that has been designed or modified to require that resistance to detonation.

To illustrate a few of the differences effecting octane requirements, here are several of the major differences between a typical kart engine and a gasoline burning V 8 racing engine:

	Kart	V-8
Compression ratio	6.5 - 7.8	10.0 - 13.5
Spark lead	20 - 25°	36 - 42°
Valve lift	.200 - .250	.300 - .600
Maximum RPM	5000 - 6500	7000 - 9000
HP per cubic inch	.42 - .58	1.1 - 1.8
Octane rating required	80 - 85	100 +

To find the gasoline that is best for the engine, chassis, track driven (altitude), and particular driving technique, is a bit time consuming, but really quite easy.

Start with the highest octane fuel that is permitted in the class. Have yourself timed (stopwatch only) for at least 10-15 laps at your best speed to determine your average lap time. Then use this fuel for one full evening of racing.

Then, next week, drop down to the next lower grade of fuel, and repeat the practice and racing experiment. If this fuel runs satisfactorily, use it for one night of racing. If it does not run satisfactorily, go back to the last fuel that was used in actual racing, and stay with it.

Continue this series of experiments until you find the lowest octane (and price) fuel that runs satisfactorily in your particular situation. Once you have pinned down the minimum octane requirement in your racing engine, with it's unique spark and valve settings, compression ratio, and normal and maximum RPM, going to an even higher octane gasoline is not going to result in the engine making any more power. It will just result in you spending extra money.

Purchasing your fuel from a manufacturer will guarantee consistency and the highest octane. Using a "racing" gasoline also ensures that should the engine run hot or lean, it will not detonate or detonate as much as it would with "pump gas". A good racing fuel also ensures consistency from batch to batch, which will make tuning easier.

Always remember that the fuel you buy may contain as many as 10 additives. The fuel that is outstanding at sea level might be flat on acceleration at altitudes above 4,000 feet. Find out from a fuel manufacturer what he advises for your altitude and compression.

Always use a large throttle return spring. The large knurled handle on the mixture adjustment screw makes adjustments easy while driving. The flat tab with the arrow is for the choke. This K & N air filter is of adequate size.

Carburetor Fine Tuning

To get the maximum performance out of a kart, you must learn to fine tune the carburetor. Since this must be done with the kart running at speed, it is difficult for the driver to do alone. Someone with a knowledge of tuning would help.

Have your tuner stand alongside the track, at various locations, while the driver runs at racing speeds. Have him listen to the exhaust as you enter turns, accelerate out of turns, and reach top speed on straights. By being 50 to 100 feet behind the kart as it runs under each of these conditions, he can get a good indication of where troubles probably exist.

At the same time, the driver must watch for, and remember, how the engine felt. Did it respond to the throttle as it should? At what RPM and what throttle position? Did it respond well after the throttle was feathered and then was stood on for a wide turn, yet it blubbered when the driver backed off then hit it after a sharp hairpin?

Were there any changes at the end of a long straight? How about during hard left turns? Hard right turns? The sound of the exhaust should be sharp and crisp anytime that power is applied. However, if it is too crisp, this probably means that the engine is running too lean at that point. Only experience will teach how to tell "crisp" from "too crisp".

Running rich on gasoline will often give a blubber coming out of the turns, but clear up to a crisp sound on the straight. Too rich on alcohol will often continue the miss

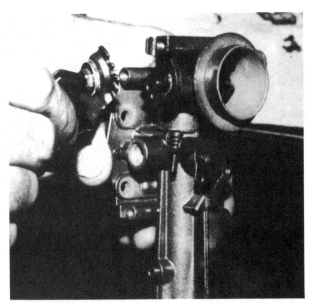

Removing the choke arm and lever.

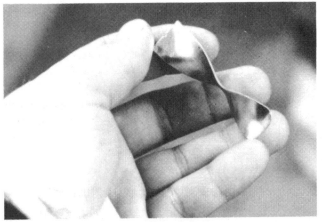

The swirl actually helps in restricted motors, and makes starting easier. It is removed in other classes of motors.

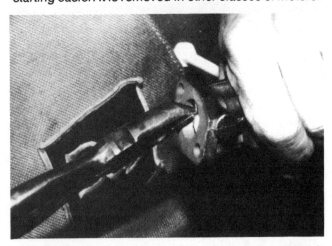

The swirl is removed with short needle nose pliers. It doesn't come out easy!

most of the way down the straight, especially in cooler weather.

The smoother the driver is in using the throttle, the easier it will be to fine tune the carburetor. The driver must remember the throttle position just before and during any problems that he, or the tuner, noticed. This will help trouble shoot the part of the carburetor which is involved.

For example, if the driver tries to pick up power gradually, and the engine seems to hesitate before suddenly responding, the problem could be in the transition from the idle to the main power circuits. Basically, the idle circuit responds to manifold vacuum, and the main jet responds to air flow through the venturi. As the throttle opens, and the manifold vacuum decreases while the airflow increases, there should be a smooth switch of the fuel feed from the idle circuit to the main circuit. Richening the idle circuit very carefully will often smooth out a rough transition from idle to power conditions.

If a hesitation is felt as the throttle is picked up, it is often caused by a low float level. On the other hand, running well at speed, but having a rough operation under yellow conditions can often be traced to a high float level.

Running fine most of the time, but experiencing hesitation or power loss at the end of a long straight, can be a fuel feed problem. The pump(s) may not be putting out enough volume, or the carburetor may have restrictions in the inlet areas (see "Fuel Systems" and "Valve Float").

An often overlooked spot in the inlet area is the clearance between the needle valve and its guide, where fuel must move through a very limited and restricted area. Drilling two small holes through this "guide", just past the needle

The mixture adjusting screw and jet require special care. They must be kept clean and the needle should not be screwed in all the way to prevent scratching it and the jet. The needle should only be open between one and two turns. Replace the jet if the needle is out of that range.

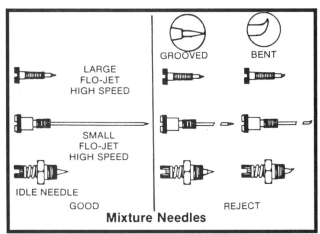

Courtesy of Briggs & Stratton

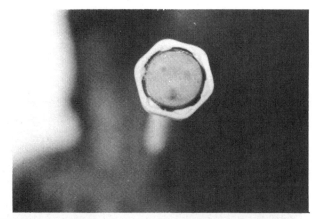

The screens at the ends of the fuel pick ups should be checked periodically. A small amount of dirt can cause tuning problems.

valve seat, will improve the fuel supply to the float bowl drastically.

Speaking of needle valves, if your carburetor has steel needles, lapping them in with toothpaste will sometimes help. Do not use valve grinding compound — it's too coarse to seal off the fuel.

Using an angle mount for the engine, will place the carburetor at an angle when the kart is on a level surface. This situation will probably require a lot of experimenta-

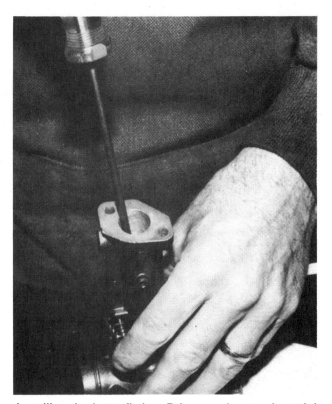

Installing the butterfly in a Briggs carburetor is a tricky job. A small amount of Loctite on the threads of the screw will prevent it from vibrating off.

tion to be certain that the float level is correct for that "unnatural" position. An angled carburetor can cause lean conditions under braking and rich condition under acceleration. Both conditions disappear when you ease off the brakes or throttle.

Remember that carburetor problems usually have a definite pattern of appearing and disappearing. Ignition problems usually show up at the same time around the track.

As one expert tuner pointed out, a winning carburetor, whether new or overhauled, still needs two special ingredients — a logic-minded tuner and a driver with a sensitive foot.

Carburetor Modifications

Some classes allow carburetor modifications. There are several things that can be done to improve performance by modifying the carburetor.

The most obvious modification is to reduce air drag and parasitic resistance, also called surface friction within the carburetor bore. The choke should be removed and the mounting holes filled with epoxy. The area should be ground and polished smooth.

File or grind the throttle butterfly to a knife edge on both sides. Grind the butterfly shaft and screw to a streamlined shape when the throttle is wide open. Grind the bore to obtain the smoothest and greatest airflow possible. When ground, the butterfly screw should be installed with Loctite to prevent its accidental loosening.

Care should be taken to ensure that the butterfly closes correctly after it has been modified. If necessary, a new butterfly should be made, from a larger carburetor if necessary. What can happen is that the bore becomes so enlarged that the butterfly no longer seats on the bore of the carburetor when the throttle is closed. Venturies should

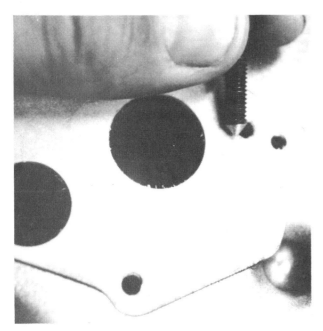

The screws holding the tank on the carburetor should be chamfered to facilitate installation.

The carburetor bore can be polished with a hand drill, or a lathe makes the job easier.

The fuel pump diaphragm cover should be surfaced — on wet and dry sandpaper dipped in solvent — to provide a perfect seal and prevent leakage.

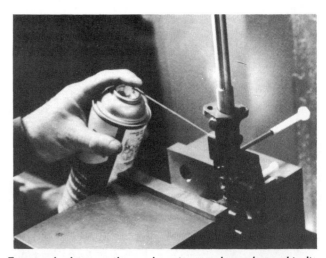

For stock classes, the carburetor can be enlarged to its maximum of 0.695-inch. A 0.693-inch reamer will allow for some error.

not be enlarged too much so as not to lose the vacuum that they create.

As it is in most racing modifications, no one can give absolute instructions regarding venturi shapes and sizes, metering system changes, etc. Trial and error are the only sure ways to go.

In carburetor modifications, as in oiling and ignition changes, keep in mind that we are demanding from two to four times what the manufacturer had in mind. For example, most 5 horsepower kart engines were originally rated at 3600 RPM, with the stipulation that they should not be run above 85% of that (or 3060 RPM) continuously.

Since these engines are regularly raced In the 6000 to 7000 RPM range, and some are run on alcohol, you can see that the carburetor alone must be changed to handle twice as much air, plus two times as much gasoline (or four times as much alcohol) as the amount of fuel and air the designer provided for.

Therefore, in modifying carburetors we must consider how and how much fuel gets into the carburetor bowl, how and how much air and fuel passes through the main and idle metering systems.

A Horstman carburetor restrictor plate for Junior classes.

A flow bench is an invaluable tool to the serious engine builder. Richard Hearn is preparing to test a Briggs carburetor.

Alcohol As Fuel

As you move up into "faster" classes, or in all classes in some racing organizations, you will be using alcohol in place of gasoline. Using alcohol successfully requires modifications to the entire fuel system.

There are several types of alcohol that can be used as racing fuel: methyl, ethyl, butyl, propyl, etc. — but methyl alcohol, or methanol, is the type used most often.

The following are some generalizations about alcohol:

1. Generally, alcohol is safer than gasoline as fuel because it resists exploding, taking 4-5 times the volume of vapor to get an equivalent reaction.

2. Alcohol is very toxic, where swallowing as little as 2 ounces is enough to be fatal unless treated immediately. Obviously, sucking on a hose to syphon alcohol or gasoline is very foolish.

3. Alcohol burns with a very pale blue, almost invisible, flame. Many fires have been burning, and people were burned, before anyone realized that there was a problem.

While methanol can be purchased from most racing fuel dealers, or from chemical supply houses, you should never just look for the lowest price. Cost per gallon increases drastically as the water content goes down. Always use the "purest" alcohol that can be located. Purchasing from a well established blender like So Cal Performance will ensure fuels of the highest and most consistent quality.

As alcohol evaporates in the intake system, it has a cooling effect. This is caused by the law of physics which dictates that energy (heat) is required to change the state of a fluid into a vapor. Alcohol happens to require 6 to 9 times the amount of heat to change its state than gasoline requires. The denser charge, resulting from this tremendous cooling of the intake mixture, is one of the greatest contributors to horsepower increases possible in an alcohol motor.

However, the popular idea that an engine runs drastically cooler on alcohol is not completely accurate. The combustion temperature of gasoline is about 3900 degrees, and that of alcohol about 3500 degrees, so the actual effect on engine temperature is minor (about 10 to 20 degrees in an air cooled engine).

You can run an overly rich alcohol mixture, and thus cool the engine somewhat, but this reduces the possible power output. An advantage realized from the cooler, denser mixture found when using alcohol is that a denser mixture resists reversion, or the feedback of exhaust gases during valve overlap.

By itself, alcohol does not offer more power, having about 8,600 BTU per pound energy, against 19,000-19,500 BTU per pound in gasoline. Simply stated, alcohol fuel allows the engine to be designed, or modified, to

Alcohol is very hard on paint and aluminum parts. Note the streaks on this tank.

produce more horsepower than it would have in un-modified form running on gasoline. However, another reason alcohol produces more power is that it is a higher octane fuel and it allows the use of higher compression ratios without detonating.

A recent report on controlled experiments before and after modifying a racing engine to run on alcohol (instead of racing gas), shows actual increases in the 2 to 14% range:

RPM	HP Increase
4000	14%
4500	13%
5000	9%
5500	8%
6000	7%
6500	5%
7000	2%

The changes to be made to utilize the full capabilities of alcohol are really quite simple, but time consuming and costly.

First, the engine will use about 2 to 2 1/2 times as much fuel as it would with gasoline, but trying to do the job by simply modifying the carburetor jet and fuel pump is not a complete job.

The jets and needle valve areas must be doubled in area, not diameter. To calculate the area of the jets and passages use the formula: 3.1416 times the radius (not the diameter) squared. Bowl capacity should be increased. All carburetor fuel passages must be enlarged. Float arms should be longer than they are with gasoline.

The biggest problems, and expenses, lie in the changes that must be made to resist the highly corrosive effect of alcohol on steel, aluminum, pot metal, magnesium, gaskets, synthetics, etc.

Fuel check station. Tech inspectors use the water mix method with alcohol or they use an electronic fuel tester to determine the legality of the fuel. These fuel testers are available from G.I.R.P.

The corrosive effect can ruin an engine in a few weeks. This means that the entire fuel system, from tank to intake valve, should be reworked by replacing parts with brass, stainless steel, or hard anodized aluminum. You can get away with replacing all those parts if the alcohol is drained immediately after a race and the whole system is flushed with gasoline. Aluminum cylinder heads, manifolds, and blocks that are used with methanol, can be expected to

The power has been known to blow the head right off the motor if one of these girdles is not used on an "open" four cycle motor.

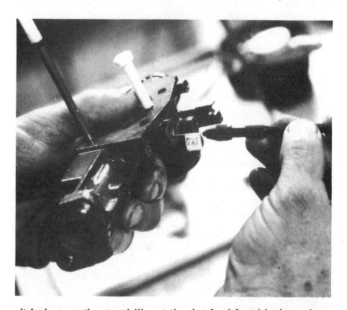

It is imperative to drill out the jet fuel feed holes when using alcohol. IKF and WKA allow drilling the smaller passage to .027-inch and the larger one to .062-inch. It is not important to drill the passages for gasoline motors.

require additional maintenance, and to have relatively shorter life spans.

The inside of the engine will require changes too. Valve guides are usually no problem, but because of the reaction of the alcohol on the hot valves, stainless steel or titanium valves are best. Any good valve will do, but you cannot just grind and set them as you would with gasoline. Alcohol has no lubricating effect for the hot exhaust valves, so these will wear against the valve seats much more rapidly. In any event, expect a lot more valve grinds than you would have with gasoline.

Cam timing requirements will change a bit, depending on the shape of the combustion chamber, and ignition timing can usually be advanced an extra 2 to 3 degrees.

Because of blow-by of alcohol into the crankcase oil, in addition to flushing the entire fuel system with gasoline after every evening of racing, you should also drain and flush the engine areas that are exposed to crankcase oil.

Special synthetic oils designed for use with alcohol will reduce this drain and flush requirement, but will not completely eliminate it. Even when using these synthetic oils, you should completely drain and flush the crankcase, valve, and cam areas at least every second or third racing evening. (Note the drain and flush procedure listed in the "Choosing an Oil" section.)

An interesting idea, for those who like to gamble, is to add one ounce of synthetic oil (or medicinal castor oil) to each gallon of methanol. This sometimes will reduce the corrosion, and lubricate the exhaust valve. However, it creates a very hard form of carbon in the combustion chamber. It still seems best to flush the entire engine if you expect to let it set for more than a day or two.

In a methanol-fueled engine, there can sometimes be starting and power problems that are hard to trace, but are cleared up by replacing an apparently good spark plug with a new one. This can usually be traced to an almost invisible coating that has been deposited, cooled, and hardened on the electrode. When this gets to about .010" thickness, the plug starts to misfire.

Burning this off by running the engine on straight gasoline after each race meet, will not only avoid the problem, but will automatically flush the entire fuel system of the corrosive alcohol.

Nitro Additives

Most speed shops and kart supply shops offer various "nitro" mixes that are always guaranteed to increase horsepower. While it is true, to an extent, that most additives will improve performance, one cannot simply dump an additive in the fuel tank and expect tremendous gains. These additives must be used very carefully as they cause increased stress on the engine. Remember that the drag racers who use nitro rebuild their engines after almost every run.

The addition of a nitro based compound to the fuel will generate as much as 10% more power, when used at the 5% mix level. That would be one part nitro to 19 parts fuel, or 6.4 ounces per gallon. The power increases because nitromethane (CH_3NO_3) and nitroparafin (CH_3NO_2) are oxygen bearing compounds, which burn hotter and more quickly than the basic gasoline or alcohol.

Of the two, nitroparafin has a slightly lower effect on power than nitromethane, but when used as in some of the commercial mixtures with ethyl ether and toluol, it is far safer and easier to use.

Adding nitro requires about .001" larger jets for each percent of nitro in your mix (for example, 5% nitro requires .005" larger jets). The ignition timing should be retarded about 1 degree for each 5% of nitro in the mix.

More than 10% nitro will give very large increases in power but the potential engine damage would be far more trouble (and expense) than the horsepower gain would be worth.

Do not run more than 5% nitro for more than 3-4 laps (qualifying) and always expect the added heat generated by the nitro to increase your engine temperature by as much as 10%.

If the engine ran hot before, adding nitro compounds will make it run even hotter yet!

Tank supports prevent the carburetors from cracking. The restrictor and gaskets move the whole assembly away from the motor and a shim needs to be installed where the arrow points.

Chapter 4

Lubrication & Ignition Systems

Choosing An Oil

Recent improvements in blending motor oils have produced light, multigrade, "racing" or "performance" lubricants designed for the high revving, turbocharged, street engines. These are excellent oils for use in racing karts.

Since these oils provide all of the protection that you need, and in the lighter grades cause less drag than the regular oils, they release more RPM, and therefore more horsepower, from the engines. The basic oil accounts for about 75 to 80 percent of what comes in the can, and it also serves as a carrier for additives.

These additives allow the oil to cool the engine more efficiently, keep the oil from thinning when it gets hot, resist corrosion, and reduce friction and foaming far better than a straight oil would provide.

This means that a lighter weight oil will do everything that you need to have done, yet will give you about 2 to 3 percent more horsepower without changing anything else.

Winston Cup stockers regularly use light grade oils such as 10-40 for qualifying and 20-50 for their races. It's the "Racing" or "Performance" oils that have all of these high

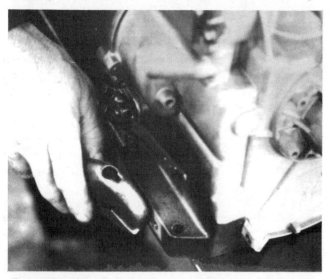

Removing the oil drain plug.

performance additives. Using one of them, changing after each evening of racing, will cost you a buck or so a week — and still give a little more horsepower at the clutch.

Synthetic oils have also shown great merit in race engines. Oils such as the Neo synthetic can be used at greater temperatures without breaking down. Oils do not get very hot in a kart engine, but should the engine overheat or run lean it will have a little insurance against seizing. Since the synthetic oils can be run much hotter it stands to reason that we could use a thinner grade of oil and achieve the same protection as we would with a heavier grade of regular oil.

Before making a final selection of an oil, test it for compatibility with the intended fuel. Take a small jar and pour into it equal amounts of your intended oil and fuel. Shake well and let it stand for 15 to 20 minutes. The oil and alcohol should mix as much as possible. Liquid fuel that has blown past the piston rings can cause several serious reactions. When using gasoline, this will wash away much of the residual oil in the bearings during times when the engine is not running, resulting in starting the engine with dry bearings. Methanol that blows by will corrode aluminum, soften gasket material, and cause foaming of the oil. If you must use a fuel/oil combination that does not pass this test, you will have to drain and flush the crankcase after every race or expect to overhaul the engine about every 3 to 4 meets.

When draining and flushing, drain the oil while the engine is hot. Put in a quart of cheap, light viscosity oil, then crank the engine a dozen or so times with the ignition off. Then drain this oil, and refill with the proper amount of your desired oil.

Always drain the oil while it is hot. Then stir the drained oil gently with a magnet and let it run through one layer of thin cloth in a funnel. The magnet will trap iron or steel particles, and the cloth will filter out aluminum, gasket scraps, etc. Knowing which is which can help identify any interior parts that are wearing more rapidly than normal.

When running an overhead valve engine, be sure the oil contains a large amount of extreme pressure additive. When installing new pushrods, rockers, or rocker pivots,

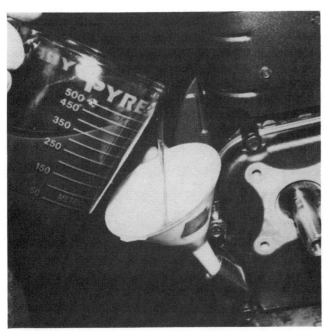

A kitchen measuring cup works well to install the oil. Briggs motors take 16 ounces. Check it on a level surface after filling. Motors on an angle mount should be raised back to level before checking the oil level.

run the engine at medium RPM (about 2500-3000) for 30 minutes to seat in the bearing surfaces and spread out the load. Many rocker failures can be traced to overlooking this practice.

Spark Plug Selection

The effect of cylinder temperature is a critically important factor in operating an engine under high output conditions. In a street engine this temperature is maintained fairly constant by the use of a thermostat in the cooling system.

In a racing, or an air cooled, engine that is run without thermostats, the outside air temperature will vary the running temperature of the engine. As a result of this variation in running temperature, a single heat range spark plug will not always give the best performance.

This means that you cannot just stick in a spark plug and run it until it begins to "miss" or becomes hard to start. Before even considering such matters as carburetor jets, one must learn to read spark plugs to determine the proper plug to be used at that moment.

A hotter plug does not produce a hotter spark, make the engine run hotter or cooler, or have any other direct effect on the way the engine runs. Neither will a cooler plug have the opposite effect. The only difference is that a "hot" plug has a longer insulator, thus retaining combustion heat at the electrodes. The "cold" plug has a shorter insulator, and dissipates the heat more rapidly.

A correct heat range plug is one that runs hot enough to burn off the carbon, oil, or lead deposits that form on the electrodes without being so hot that it allows the electrodes to burn away prematurely, become red hot, or cause preignition.

If the plug is too cold, it will not burn away these normal cylinder deposits (carbon, oil, and lead) which will coat the insulator and electrodes and cause misfiring.

Too hot a plug can cost races through preignition, or can cause detonation, which can destroy an engine in a few seconds. Too cold a plug will gradually foul, and leave a sluggish running engine.

To "read" a plug, put 5 to 10 laps of hard driving on a clean plug. Then "cut clean." That is, cut the ignition while at full throttle, then keep the throttle wide open while coasting into the pits. Pull the plug immediately, and look for either (or both) of these colors:

Gray or tan tint: A mild gray or tan color on the insulator tip is normal in a gasoline fueled engine.

Heat coloration: A bluish area, similar to the color of overheated metal, should show on the center electrode, about .025" from the tip. The side electrode should also develop this color, ending near the curved portion of the electrode. To look for this, lightly scrape the electrode.

On a very hot day, since the engine temperature will run somewhat above normal, a one or two step cooler plug may be needed. This will conduct the combustion heat away from the electrodes more rapidly, keeping the electrode operating temperature within the desired range for best operation (700 degrees F at idle, to 1500 degrees F at full power).

On an unusually cool day, or evening, with the resulting lower engine temperature, a hotter plug might be required.

A recent series of tests indicates noticeable increases in power as plug gaps are increased, up to the point where either misfiring begins, or up to .100" gap, whichever comes first. This is because of the longer "lightening bolt" between the electrodes.

Experiment with spark plug gaskets to "index" the plug. Try to get the open area, between the electrodes, aimed toward the center of the combustion area in the cylinder. This will only give about 1-2% more power, but every little bit helps.

Another tip: Inspect new plugs before installing them. Sometimes plugs will have a slight burr where the ground electrode is welded to the shell. This will damage or strip the threads in the cylinder head. Filing down the burrs will correct this situation.

Finally, never use a long reach plug in an engine that was designed for short threaded plugs. Some people claim that this raises the compression slightly, but sooner or later the extra threads will burn or carbon over. Then when the plug is removed it will also remove the threads in the head. The longer reach plug may, with some engines, come in contact with the piston. Some racers have used that trick success-

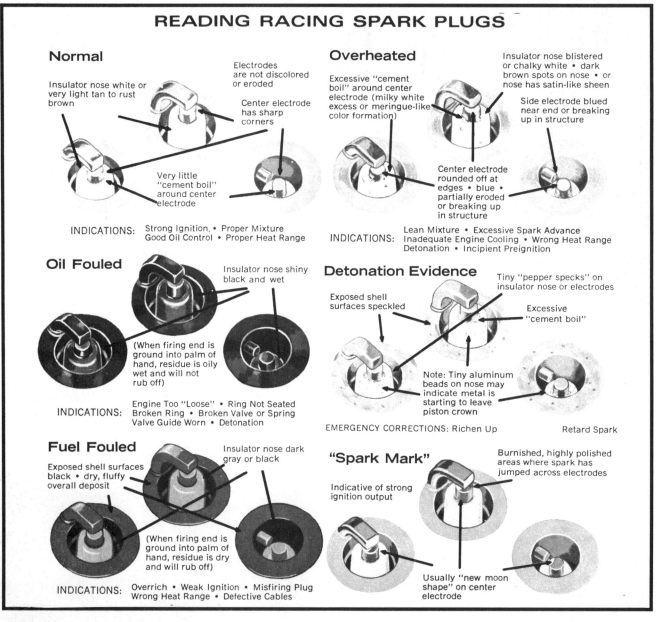

READING RACING SPARK PLUGS

Normal

Insulator nose white or very light tan to rust brown

Electrodes are not discolored or eroded

Center electrode has sharp corners

Very little "cement boil" around center electrode

INDICATIONS: Strong Ignition • Proper Mixture Good Oil Control • Proper Heat Range

Overheated

Insulator nose blistered or chalky white • dark brown spots on nose • or nose has satin-like sheen

Excessive "cement boil" around center electrode (milky white excess or meringue-like color formation)

Side electrode blued near end or breaking up in structure

Center electrode rounded off at edges • blue • partially eroded or breaking up in structure

INDICATIONS: Lean Mixture • Excessive Spark Advance Inadequate Engine Cooling • Wrong Heat Range Detonation • Incipient Preignition

Oil Fouled

Insulator nose shiny black and wet

(When firing end is ground into palm of hand, residue is oily wet and will not rub off)

INDICATIONS: Engine Too "Loose" • Ring Not Seated Broken Ring • Broken Valve or Spring Valve Guide Worn • Detonation

Detonation Evidence

Tiny "pepper specks" on insulator nose or electrodes

Exposed shell surfaces speckled

Excessive "cement boil"

Note: Tiny aluminum beads on nose may indicate metal is starting to leave piston crown

EMERGENCY CORRECTIONS: Richen Up   Retard Spark

Fuel Fouled

Insulator nose dark gray or black

Exposed shell surfaces black • dry, fluffy overall deposit

(When firing end is ground into palm of hand, residue is dry and will rub off)

INDICATIONS: Overrich • Weak Ignition • Misfiring Plug Wrong Heat Range • Defective Cables

"Spark Mark"

Burnished, highly polished areas where spark has jumped across electrodes

Indicative of strong ignition output

Usually "new moon shape" on center electrode

---

fully on two cycles, but the reason this was used was to introduce the spark closer to the piston as it came up the cylinder, causing an effect similar to advancing the ignition timing.

Ignition Systems

While dealing with the electrical system of a kart engine, it might be well to cover an area of much disagreement, and then offer a couple of tips.

There are some people in karting who believe that since a magneto has points, it is not desireable for karts, because they feel that the points will "bounce" at high RPMs. In this regard, a little mental arithmetic will provide an answer.

In automobiles the ignition points open and close four times per revolution (in a typical V8). To achieve this, the distributor and point cam turn at half engine speed. Thus in a V8, at 5000 RPM the points open and close 4 times per revolution, or 20,000 times a minute. Yet these cars are driven at that speed, and very rarely (if ever) have any problems.

On the other hand, a one cylinder engine usually has the point cam on the crankshaft, causing the points to operate once per revolution. This means that the kart points operate 5000 times per minute at 5000 RPM — one fourth the frequency that is found in a bigger engine.

The exception to this rule is the kart engine that was built with a pushrod operating the points. In this design, points are a bad idea, because the weight of the pushrod will

Arrow points to the line that must match the armature. The dial indicator should read about 0.185 to 0.205-inch before top dead center. This corresponds to 29 to 30 degrees before top dead center. The flywheel must be moved to set the timing.

cause point bounce at speed. If it is available, CDI ignition is best for these engines.

However, CDI is not a "cure-all". Here are some of the differences between magnetos and CDIs:

Magneto

Advantages: Constant intensity sparks through the entire RPM range, easy maintenance and adjustment.

Disadvantages: Harder starting, need polarity check at installation.

C.D.I.

Advantages: Easy starting, no routine adjustments.

Disadvantages: Spark intensity falls off at high RPMs, expensive when replacing components. Heat and vibration sensitive.

It might be remembered that practically all midgets, TQs, and sprint cars use magnetos. If your kart engine uses a magneto, and you want the best spark setting that you can get, you will have to do some experimenting. But first, something about ignition systems that you should keep in mind.

In an old style automotive points system, the amount of point gap, and the time that the points open, are both important. The amount of the gap controls the time that the points are open and closed. This controls the time that the battery has to charge the coil. The instant that the points open is the time that the spark occurs. The moment at which the points open in relationship to the piston is adjusted by turning the distributor.

In a magneto, the coil is charged by the movement of the magnet. Here the force of the magnetic field (therefore coil saturation) goes up as the RPM goes up. This means that the amount that the points open is not significant.

Timing Adjustment

In a magneto, the instant that the points open still controls the timing. Some magnetos can be turned like a distributor to adjust this timing, but most kart engines have the magneto built into the flywheel, which means that the timing must be adjusted in another fashion.

Using a piece of .001" shim stock as a feeler gauge, adjust the points so that they just begin to open at the point where you want the spark to take place. Try various advanced and retarded settings, until your test driving shows that you have the best possible operation. Mark the flywheel to match.

For example, the shop manual for one kart engine states that the points should open at 20 degrees before top dead center. Experiments show a noticeable performance increase at 26 degrees, but the improvement begins to drop off at 28 degrees.

The air gap under the armature should be 0.010-inch. Paper 0.010-inch thick will work for measuring.

Finger points to wire that kill switch should be connected to. Note engine kill switch in background.

For best results in setting the spark timing, be certain that the TDC mark matches the exact moment that the piston reaches top dead center.

Ignition Kill Switch

Another item in the ignition system that can prevent injury and damage to the engine if the throttle spring breaks, is a kill switch. Mount an ignition switch (toggle type) directly above the steering wheel, positioned so that the toggle is in the up position when the engine is running. For a twin engine kart, use a double pole single throw switch. With the switch installed this way, a downward slap will stop the engine(s) instantly when needed.

Carburetor Jetting

Once you have determined the proper heat range plug for the engine, then it can be read for clues as to proper fuel/air mixture. Always keep in mind that a larger jet will give a richer mixture, and a smaller one leans out the mix. To find out how the mixture is at any particular moment, run 5 to 10 laps at speed, cut clean, and pull the plug while it is still hot. If the mixture is extremely rich the plug might even show signs of wet fuel. However, this is usually caused by too cold a plug, the engine and plug not being completely warmed up, or permitting some idling while trying to "cut clean".

If the engine is just running a little too rich, the insulator will appear to be covered with soot of a dark brown to black color. If the tips of both electrodes are clean, this means that it is firing properly and the problem is in the jetting. However, if the tips are not clean, the plug is carbon fouled and should be replaced.

If the mixture is too lean, there might not be enough color to permit accurate reading. The electrode might show a chalky-white shade, or even be burned to a bluish color overall. Remember that too lean produces very high cylinder temperatures, which might show signs similar to too hot a plug, or even signs of detonation (cracked insulator or burned electrodes).

The spark plug in a properly tuned engine will have a tan or grayish color on the side electrode, and a light brown at the shoulder of the insulator down where it meets the plug shell.

Chapter 5

EXPERIMENTING

As you progress up into faster racing classes, you will be allowed to make various modifications to your engine. Unfortunately, if you are like most of us, you do not have a dynamometer on which you can test your engine. Professional kart engine builders such as Hearn Competition Karting in Arcadia, California will dyno test motors for customers and supply recommendations. Doing this will save many hours of tuning and money that would normally be spent on experimental parts, blown engines, cams, etc. There are other reputable engine builders throughout the country that will do the same.

Fortunately, of similar use to dyno readings are the results that you can attain on the race track. Here, a planned experimental program can give you many advantages over those who just want to jump in their kart and race.

During the winter months, and other times when there is no racing that occupies your mind, take time to do a lot of thinking. Reading other books on other subjects from Steve Smith Autosports will often generate some ideas that can be used in karting. Even reading books on two stroke motors such as "Racing The Yamaha KT100" or beginner's books such as "The Beginner's Complete Karting Guide," also published by Steve Smith Autosports, will kindle some food for thought and those readings may reveal some tricks you can adapt to your form of racing. Reading on suspension technology such as in "Stock Car Chassis Technology" will teach the basics of handling and suspension dynamics, basics which also apply to karting.

Another tremendous source of information, in language that any eighth grader can understand, is in the tech articles run in **Circle Track, Open Wheel and Stock Car Racing** magazines. These deal with almost every technical subject, present good and bad points of conflicting opinions, and usually cover concepts that can be applied to four-cycle karting.

Look over your organization rules for places where you might gain some advantage. Where ranges are given, rather than exact measurements, consider whether the "high end" or the "low end" of that range will be most beneficial to you. For example, if your valve setting specifies .005-.010", plan on trying to run the .005" setting, and then the .010" measurement.

Before the racing season starts, test everything that you can think of against the stop watch. Keep records of each test, so that later you will know what effect a setting or combination had.

Hearn Competition Karting uses this dyno to test the motors they build and to break them in.

Reading other books such as these, from Steve Smith Autosports, will kindle more thoughts for tips and tricks to improve your racing.

These crates can be built to carry spare motors.

During the regular season you will have a chance to experiment and to learn what a particular combination will do under actual racing conditions. Here are several cases that produced very good results:

1. One driver knew that he had his class championship won because mathematically no one could catch him. He spent the last six weeks of the season experimenting under racing conditions. On one occasion he tried a carburetor that was illegal in his class, but legal in a faster class. By racing "not for points" that night, he ran the carburetor on a kart with everything else "normal". This way, he knew exactly what the carburetor, by itself, would do to performance.

Of course he did not win many races during this period, but with the championship already guaranteed he was more interested in what he could learn than he was in building up points.

2. Another driver knew that his chassis/engine combination was outclassed by his competition. He viewed that season as a time for learning, trying every change that he thought might help him. By the end of the season he had an upgraded combination that consistently ran in the top five in his class. With the newer chassis that he planned on buying during the winter months, and the things that he had learned about that engine, and about chassis set-up and modifications, he looked forward to winning his share of races the next year.

3. Several drivers combined resources to test various set ups under actual racing conditions. The way they did this was by renting a track and making changes to only one kart and checking the performance against another and against the stop watch. That way they could test something, tear down and rebuild, and test again, all without having the pressures of racing.

In each of these cases the drivers learned the facts about what would work and what would not. They did not have to rely on rumors or old wives tales.

The point is that nothing remains completely static in racing. As you move to another class, buy a new chassis, convert to a different engine, work with a new mechanic or engine builder, or just learn new driving techniques, you will need specific knowledge to take full advantage of these changes.

If you want to, you can learn those things the hard way. You can just drive in the regular races, trying to learn as you go, and hope that you eventually will be one of those drivers that others envy.

Or, you can go about it the smart way. Take the time to think, to plan, and to experiment, condensing several years of seat-of-the-pants learning into the much shorter time of a systematic approach.

But be very careful to avoid being so impressed by one result that you overlook the total situation. For example, one combination may yield higher RPM at the end of the straight but the same combination will lug the engine coming off the turns. Even if this shows an improvement on the stop watch, the driver might get passed coming out of the turns. This is where compromising comes into play. Another set up might show some improvement on the clock, but the engine would bog down if the driver were to get stuck in traffic. Here a conservative approach might be better especially if the driver is not very experienced.

If a change reduces your test lap times over a series of four laps (averaged), or it has proven to improve your average finishing position, then use it. Otherwise, consider that particular change to be among the experiments that didn't work and should be forgotten, or that need further thinking.

Remember, it's not top speed alone that is needed, or just acceleration. What wins consistently is a combination that includes both of these, in a drivable compromise.

Using the Tach

If you are serious about racing, you must get a tach/temp gauge. G.I.R.P puts out several units, one even incorporates tach, head temperature and an exhaust temperature readout. To make full use of these instruments, you must train yourself to read the indications accurately, and remember when and where each number appeared.

Many drivers say that they do not have time to read numbers while they are racing. While it is true that the first lap or two can get quite busy for a driver, it is possible during the rest of the race to pre-select, during practice,

Tach and temperature gauges are invaluable instruments for the serious karter.

Third bearings like this one are required by most racing associations. The crankshafts used to break from the weight of the clutch. At 12,000 to 14,000 RPM the loose clutches became deadly projectiles. Note the fin saver guard on this motor. These guards save the fins when the chains break.

some spots where a quick glance can be given to the gauges. Practicing quick eye movements just sitting still in the kart at home is a good exercise.

One big advantage in using a tach is that it can be determined, with reasonable accuracy, the three most important RPM values for an engine. Find a smooth, fairly level, section of pavement where you can run straight ahead for a hundred yards or so. From a dead stop, open the throttle very slowly, concentrating on the feeling of acceleration as you gain speed.

When you notice that the rate of acceleration seems to start increasing, note the RPM figure. This is the bottom end of the effective engine torque. Continue this slow increase in speed until the rate seems to be falling off. This is the top end of the effective torque range. Keep on accelerating slowly until it appears that the kart is still gaining speed, but the engine seems to be running out of pep. This is the top effective horsepower speed. Your engine builder should be able to give you ball park figures as to where these peaks are. Repeat this experiment several times, writing down the three RPM figures each time, until you can see a definite pattern in the numbers.

Without a dynamometer, you have learned how your engine actually puts out the power. You can use this knowledge to match the clutch to the engine.

Setting the Clutch to the Power Curve

Before attempting to set the clutch, the engine and clutch should be warmed up. Take the kart out and drive it at about the speed your seat-of-the-pants tells you is just below the speed at which the clutch should engage. Floor the gas pedal and look at the tach. The numbers will click up and they will suddenly stabilize. That is where the clutch grabbed. Most stock engines seem to work best with a clutch setting of 3400 to 3600 RPM. This RPM is about the torque peak on most motors. Your engine builder should have more experience in this area and he should be consulted to be sure the clutch is set to match the particular torque curve of his engine.

Do not attempt to set the clutch with your foot on the brake and the other on the gas while standing still in the pits. This will give a false reading and it will damage the clutch. Also, if your track has a long uphill, avoid slipping the clutch during the climb to prevent potential damage to the clutch. In theory, not having a transmission in a kart, you would want the clutch to start engaging (slipping) at about the bottom of the middle third of the torque range. You would also want it to engage fully (grip) at about the middle of the total torque range. In practice, this is not always possible.

If you have a **very** sensitive throttle foot, you can adjust your clutch to give **the effect** of a transmission. On a smooth and level stretch of pavement, with the kart stopped, **very gradually** move the throttle toward the open position. Note the tach reading as the kart begins to

Axle clutches are not very popular in sprint karting. The cost is one drawback, and they are not as much of an advantage in sprint racing as they are in road racing.

move. Stop, then floor the throttle while watching the tach. The two readings will give you the "slipping" and the "gripping" RPMs.

Even the most basic centrifugal clutch can be adjusted to some extent. While the two variables interrelate to each other, and neither is fully in control of any aspect of clutch

actions, these two rules are the basis of all centrifugal clutch adjustment:

1. The spring (or springs) have the greatest effect on the RPM at which the clutch begins to engage.

2. The number and weight of the rotating weights (shoes) have the greatest effect on full engagement.

As an example of what can be done, even with a "non adjustable" clutch, a well known, very basic, clutch was adjusted as follows:

Twelve (12) coils were removed from the retraction spring. Three shoes were removed, and the remaining three evenly spaced within the clutch. The result of this was that engagement started at about 3200 RPM, and full engagement took place at about 3600 RPM.

Knowing these RPM readings for your particular clutch will allow you to use it in the same manner that you slip the clutch on a family car when starting on a steep hill. But always remember to use this technique **only** when it is of a distinct advantage to you, because it increases clutch wear markedly.

Setting Idle RPM

Knowing the speed at which the clutch begins to engage will dictate what idle RPM is best for racing (forget what the engine manufacturer recommends for rototiller or lawnmower use). Just set the idle speed to about 200 to 300 RPM below the speed where your clutch starts to take hold. This way, the engine will not slow down as much when the driver backs off for a turn. This allows it to start putting out power much quicker than it would if idling down to about 1200 to 1400 RPM. This rapid acceleration and engagement can give as much as 1/2-second jump on the guys who must coast while waiting for their engines to regain racing speed.

Knowing your "best" RPM figures will help you in being quicker and more accurate in deciding what gear changes might be needed. A tachometer can be invaluable, in testing, adjusting, and practice.

Chapter 6

ENGINE BUILDING

Anyone with a fair set of tools, and reasonable patience and skill, can assemble an engine that will be satisfactory for street, or for "strictly stock" use. However, as you move up into classes where aftermarket parts and other major modifications are allowed, the situation becomes more complex and this is where you will need an engine builder, rather than an assembler.

Some racers will simply order a bunch of parts that look good in a catalog, or that someone has praised during a bench racing session. He will then assemble the engine himself, or hire someone to assemble the parts. On the other hand, the serious and knowledgeable racer knows that whether he builds the engine himself, or hires a professional builder for the job, there is a lot of serious thinking and careful planning to accomplish before the first part is ordered or modified. For instance, a Cosworth or Chevrolet built for an Indy car would not be very practical in a NASCAR sedan at Darlington, and vice versa. The

A brand new Briggs 130232. This model is more desirable because it comes with a roller bearing in the side cover.

particular chassis that the engine is in, the personal driving style, and (more importantly) the track or tracks that will be driven on, must all be considered in deciding how to assemble what parts, in what modified form, as an engine is built.

Suppose, for example, most of your driving will be done on short ovals, or on tracks with short straights and tight turns. Here you would be at full throttle much of the time, but backing off as you approach and enter each of these turns. This engine should be built and geared to operate in a fairly limited RPM range, staying in the upper portion of the horsepower curve.

On other tracks, with long straights and sweeping curves, your throttle is wide open most of the time, just feathering momentarily to set up your front end for one of the curves. Here you'll want the RPM spread from where the horsepower begins to level off, to a point 5-15% above peak horsepower. Tracks with long straights and tight curves create drastic speed variations. These need an engine that pulls smoothly from low in the torque range to as high as possible in the horsepower range.

Of course most cars have transmissions, which will accept these variations in tracks while keeping the engine in the upper horsepower range. However, most karts run with a single ratio between engine RPM and wheel RPM. Therefore you must build the engines and gear to the track(s) that you will be driving on.

Before building an engine a few things should be determined:

1) The budget available.

2) The experience level of the driver will, to an extent, determine how much should be spent on a motor. A novice in his first year of racing may wish to have a motor built for reliability with power as a secondary consideration. The beginner will probably also want an engine that is easy to tune and will not require as much attention as a faster engine would.

3) The type of track the engine will be raced on.

4) The class the engine will be raced in. This will determine the rules that must be followed and the competitive-

Cam, valves, crankshaft, connecting rod, piston and rings. The basic motor is here. Note the rod bolt locking tab.

ness of the class can help determine how extensively the motor should be modified.

Most drivers need and want an engine that will be competitive, able to run near (or at) the front in most races, yet lasting a reasonable time before it needs a complete overhaul or simple freshening. The "engine assembler" seldom considers any of these things. The "engine builder" sees them as his most critical specifications.

Remember that the engine builder will prepare motors to the customer's unique specifications, with the unspoken understanding that as horsepower and RPM increase, so

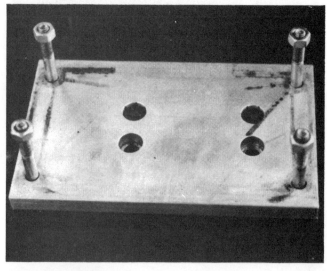

A motor stand can be built out of aluminum. This one is bolted to a bench top.

will the need for overhauls or freshening. Reliability will also decrease and the chances of finishing races will be jeopardized. This is probably the biggest compromise that you will have to face, as you move up from novice classes into the faster classes of any motor vehicle racing.

Engine Tear-Down and Inspection

Tearing down a racing engine involves a few things that may be overlooked when working with an "everyday" engine. Cleanliness, being certain that each reusable part will be returned to the same location and relationship, and inspection to determine whether the part should be reused, are of great importance to the future life and performance of that engine.

The first thing that should be done after removing the engine from the kart, is to take it to a do-it-yourself car wash. Remove the oil filler caps and drain plugs, and wash the engine completely using soapy water first, then rinse it. Wash and rinse into each oil hole, about 5-10 seconds at a time.

Do not worry about leaving water inside of it if it will be disassembled immediately.

Clean, dry, and inspect each item as it is removed from the engine. Unless you have had experience with this particular model engine, have some cans, muffin tins, egg boxes, etc., into which you can sort the parts as they pass inspection. Keep a note pad nearby and jot down any of the parts that need replacing. This will help your buying missions, before you assemble the engine.

Inspect each nut, bolt, retainer, etc., as it is removed, putting anything that "should" be replaced in with your other items for replacement. If you fear confusion later, make a list of the things that you decided to replace (such as 1 cylinder head nut, 1 side plate bolt, etc.). That way you will know where to look for the missing parts when you start assembly.

Mark each part of the valve train after it has been cleaned. Masking tape and a waterproof pen works here. After inspection, you must replace each of these parts in their previous place. You do not want to have a lifter that has been running against an intake lobe replaced on the exhaust side, or a pushrod put in upside down or with the wrong rocker arm. Remember that no two of these parts wear exactly the same, and putting the engine together with mismatched parts is asking for early failures.

With overhead valve motors, inspect each pushrod carefully, using a hand magnifying glass if possible. Remember the extreme pressure, and poor oiling, that these parts are submitted to in racing.

Be certain that each pushrod is perfectly straight (roll it on a smooth surface several times), and that each end shows no wear. Replacement now will be much cheaper than it will be later. Check each rocker arm for smooth

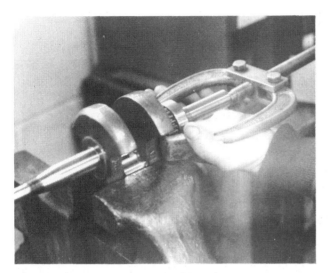

Removing the crank gear and bearing.

Briggs side cover and crank bearing.

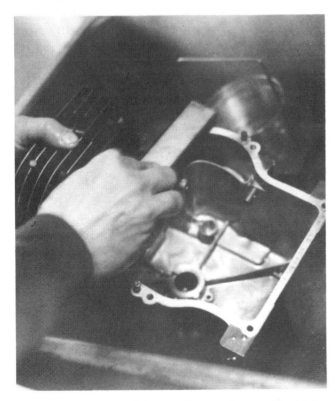

The side cover and its mating surfaces should be cleaned up with a stone and some solvent.

The stock classes require that all the sheetmetal be in place.

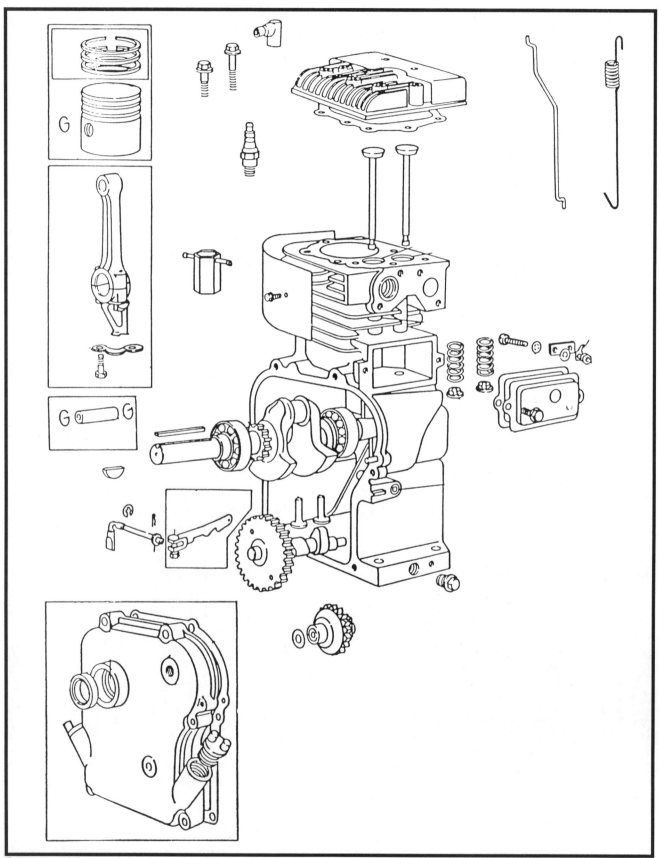

Courtesy of Briggs & Stratton

The Four Stroke Cycle

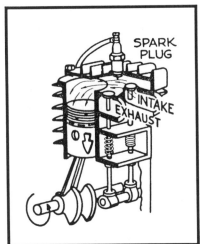

1) INTAKE STROKE. With the exhaust valve closed and the intake valve open, the piston goes down, creating a vacuum in the cylinder which draws the air/fuel mixture into the space above the piston.

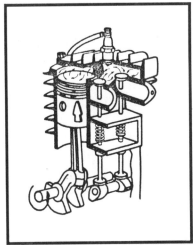

2) COMPRESSION STROKE. The intake valve closes and the piston moves upward, compressing the air/fuel mixture into the small space between the top of the piston and the cylinder head.

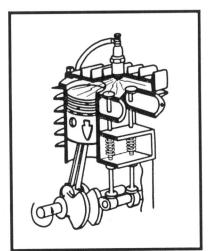

3) POWER STROKE. The magneto sends a high tension current to the spark plug, igniting the compressed mixture. The explosion expands the gases and pushes the piston down.

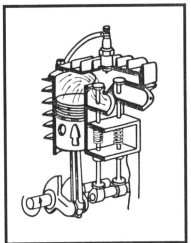

4) EXHAUST STROKE. The exhaust valve opens and the upward stroke of the piston forces all of the burnt gases out of the cylinder, completing the power cycle.

Drawings courtesy of Briggs & Stratton

This washer, under the governor gear, can cause the engine to blow if it is not removed when the governor is discarded. The washer is easily mistaken for the case itself and it can easily be overlooked.

Arrow points to the governor shaft hole that was plugged up.

operation before you remove it from the trunion. Then inspect the rubbing surfaces of both the rocker and the trunion, looking for localized polished spots, chipping, or grooves. Any rocker arm, trunion, or pushrod that shows abnormal wear should call for all three parts being replaced.

Check external gasket surfaces, looking for any signs of leakage. You might need to have these surfaces refaced, or use double gaskets.

Study the head gasket, and the gasket surfaces of the head and block, looking for any signs of combustion gas leakage. If you find any problems, schedule the block and head for resurfacing.

If your organization rules forbid removal of metal, show the gasket, head, and block to the chief tech inspector, asking for permission to have just enough ground off to get a good seal. Have your machining order worded that way, and signed off by the machinist and the chief technical inspector, when the job has been completed and keep it.

Study the combustion pattern on the head and the piston top, and store the information for use later if you are going to port the passages, modify the combustion chamber, or index the sparkplug.

When the connecting rod is removed, disconnect it from the piston and replace the cap and bolts. Schedule it for alignment at your favorite engine shop. The crank and wrist pin bearings must be perfectly parallel to each other, or the piston will be trying to bend back and forth as it goes up and down.

Check the cam lobes and gears. Any wear that you can see or feel with your fingertip or fingernail is grounds for replacement.

Check the crank and the rod bearing with a micrometer. You can probably get by with .002-.003" wear, but .004-.006" is asking for early bearing failure.

Check the piston for wear on the skirt in the areas below and 90 degrees from the wrist pin. Any wear or scratches

Checking connecting rod straightness. Tolerance of only 0.001-inch is allowed.

A solvent tank comes in very handy for cleaning. Parts can also be cleaned in soap and water, rinsed off and blown dry.

that can be felt with a fingernail warrant replacing the piston.

Check the cylinder wall, looking for remnants of "cross hatching" (a very fine criss-cross pattern) in the area where the piston rings rub. If any scratches are found in the direction of piston movement, the cylinder will need to be rebored and a new piston installed.

You can continue to run the engine if it has minor scratches in the cylinder wall below the ring rubbing area, but this will probably cause the piston to wear more rapidly than normal.

Remove all traces of carbon, or other deposits, from the head, piston, and intake and exhaust ports. An aluminum wire wheel on an electric drill will do the job, although glass beading (if permitted by your organization) is best. In cleaning the piston, be certain that the ring grooves are cleaned but be very careful not to remove any metal, particularly from the sides of the ring grooves. If you do not have a ring groove cleaner, break one of the old rings and use it as a scraper.

Finally, while the various items are receiving their scheduled machine work, carefully check your entire ignition system. Look for cracked insulation, signs of arcing, broken strands in the wiring, etc. Then clean and rebuild the carburetor and fuel pump.

If this all seems like a lot of work to get the engine torn apart, remember that racing kart engines run 1.5 to 3 times as fast as they were built to run, putting out anywhere from 20% to 100% more horsepower than the manufacturer expected. This causes a lot of stress on the parts and the slightest imperfection may cause a failure. If an engine is to be a top performer and it is built to last, you must work carefully with a lot of attention to details.

Do-It-Yourself Engines

If you decide to do your own mechanical work, whether simply assembling a stock engine or building a modified one, certain basic considerations should always be kept in mind.

First, it should be remembered that a racing engine will be assembled and disassembled many times during its life, so careful advance planning is mandatory to facilitate future work. You will find that there are many differences between putting together a racing engine, and doing a "ring and valve job" on the family automobile.

Of primary importance is the matter of cleaning engine parts. This careful cleaning of all parts (including nuts, bolts, and washers), whether new or recently disassembled, aids your inspection for wear, cracks, burrs, etc. It also takes off corrosion and deposits that can knock out bearings and bushings in a hurry.

Use solvent for the basic cleaning. Never use gasoline, which leaves a film on metal and is highly flammable. Caustic cleaners, such as commercial carburetor "boil-out" cleaners, will eat aluminum and magnesium castings if left in for even a few minutes too long. Spray-type carburetor cleaners will get into awkward or small places, but will leave a film when they evaporate. Spray-type brake cleaners air-dry without leaving deposits, but they are quite expensive. A wire wheel on a bench grinder or hand drill works well on hardened deposits, but will gouge into aluminum easily, and even dig into cast iron pistons. Glass beading is best, if it is allowed within the rules. However, remember that you will have to strip the glass particles that tend to impregnate soft metals.

Glass particles love to remain in valve guides, aluminum castings, valve passages — anything made of a soft metal — just waiting to grind things to bits as soon as the engine is started. Solvent and chemical cleaners will not even touch these abrasive bits. The only sure way to get them all off is to scrub each part with a lot of hot, soapy water, then flush clean with more hot water.

Spend the money to buy some special tools, and learn how to use them. Items such as a good dial caliper, a depth gauge, a couple of micrometers, and an inch/pound torque wrench, will lay the ground work for a professional job.

Short cuts such as plasti-gauge and "a feel for tightening bolts evenly" will never give the results that good tools, properly used, will.

An urgent need is to find a good machine shop, or preferably an experienced engine builder such as Richard Hearn who worked with us on this book. You will have to hire someone for much of the work anyway, since few of us have a complete shop available for our use, so you might as well get the best.

The few dollars difference between using a run-of-the-mill automotive shop and a well known speed or FAA-rated

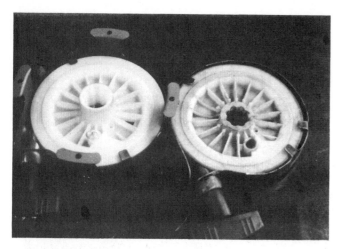

Stock starter on the left and modified starter on the right. The mounting legs have been cut off to allow the starter to be removed.

machine shop can mean the difference between one engine build-up or overhaul, and five or six of them. An experienced engine builder who does not mind doing machining for racers will also save money since his shop is already equipped with the tools and gauges needed for the particular operations. This will also cut down on the set-up time and improve the quality of the work. Many of the photos in this book were taken at Hearn Competition Karting. Many of the parts were sent by racers who did not have the necessary machines or equipment to do their own machining, but who were knowledgeable enough to assemble a motor.

Studs

A racing engine should always use studs where possible. This is especially true in kart engines where bolts screw into threads in aluminum heads, blocks, side plates, and connecting rods.

A little analysis will show that while such a bolt pulls against soft metal threads in the base structure, a properly installed stud becomes a part of the structure itself.

Always use high grade studs. This is no place to save a buck. Be sure that each stud hangs up at the end of it's threads instead of bottoming in the threaded hole. Loctite or epoxy should only be applied when ready for final assembly. Incidentally, a trick to use for disassembly on threads that have been "Loctited" is to use a little heat from a butane torch. After a gentle tap with a plastic hammer, the stud or bolt will come loose.

Assembly Tips

When rules permit, follow these tips to improve performance and assembly ease.

The stock slinger on the left should not be used on race motors. The Horstman unit on the right is much sturdier and it is inexpensive.

If the combustion chamber is larger than the cylinder bore, whether all the way around (overhead engine), or just on one side (flathead), chamfer that exposed part of the cylinder rim just enough (.020-.030" deep) to break off the sharp edge to prevent a hot spot.

Since a kart engine operates without an oil pump, a lot of attention must be given to how the splash system lubricates the various parts. Study the inside of the engine, and visualize how the oil splashes around the various parts at high RPM. Using a high speed grinder, smooth any places that would slow the return of oil to the bottom of the engine where the dipper can pick it up again.

If your engine has it's crankcase vent coming out of a section of the valve train, this indicates that the blow-by from the rings is expected to carry an oil mist into that area. It may be possible to enlarge existing holes, or create new holes, to increase the amount of oil that the splash and blow-by normally carries to this part of the engine.

Most kart connecting rods can stand improvements in their oiling. Enlarge existing oil holes to 5/32", and chamfer both ends of each hole. In some cases there are no existing holes in the wrist pin end of the rod. In that case, drill two holes, 45 degrees apart, centered on top of the rod.

Be sure that the wrist pin fits properly in both the piston and rod. A clearance of .0008" to .0010" is perfect. Also be sure that the wrist pin has .004" to .005" end play after the pin locks have been installed.

When installing piston rings, be sure that each ring can be rotated freely in it's groove, and that each ring can be pushed back into it's groove until it is perfectly flush with the piston surface, or not more than .005" below that surface.

The rod big end being honed to 0.003-inch clearance.

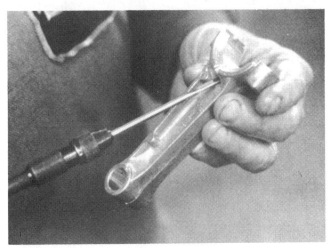

The oil hole can be drilled out to 0.156-inch. Use a 0.154-inch reamer to be safe.

Measuring the ring end gap with a feeler gauge.

A piston being used to install a ring in the bore to be checked for end gap.

Set your ring gaps for a minimum clearance of .003" per inch of cylinder diameter (regardless of what the manufacturer advises).

The extra gap will enable the ring to expand when it gets hot. If the gap is too small, the ends of the ring will collide and the ring will break. Our consulting engine builder, Richard Hearn of Hearn Competition Karting in Arcadia, California, sets the top ring on the Briggs at .008" using a .010" oversize ring that is filed down.

Push each ring about one inch down in the cylinder, using an old piston to assure that the ring is perfectly level in the cylinder. Measure the existing gap with a feeler gauge, file the ends as necessary, and recheck. This takes time and slow filing, and usually 3 to 5 trials for each ring, but this procedure is essential for maximum power and life of the engine.

When assembling an engine, every part should fit easily, without force. If a part does not fit easily, find out why by careful measurement and visual inspection. Forcing a part will cause binding and galling, which will lead to a failure.

Use a ring installation tool to put the rings on the piston, if this is at all possible. When rings are spread by hand they often develop cracks in the inner circumference. These rings can be counted on to break soon after they are placed under load.

54

The maximum piston protrusion allowed in stock classes is 0.005-inch. It can be checked with a straight edge across the piston top and feeler gauges on the block deck.

Setting Top Dead Center

During trial assembly, before the head is installed, mount the flywheel and key on the crankshaft and check the top dead center marking. The TDC mark must be perfect if the cam and the ignition are to be set correctly.

Turn the crank until the piston comes up to exactly .200" below the deck of the block (use the dial caliper or depth gauge to measure this). Scribe a mark on the flywheel exactly opposite the TDC mark on the crankcase. Then repeat, turning the crank the opposite direction, and make another mark.

The TDC mark on the flywheel should be exactly half way between your two scribe marks. If it does not match, repeat the whole affair to be sure, and if necessary make a new TDC mark.

Head Clearance

Put some small bits of modeling clay anywhere that the piston or valves appear to come close to the head or to each other. Plastic kitchen wrap on each side of the clay will keep it from sticking.

Install a used head gasket, the valves, and the head, and tighten the head studs wrist tight. Turn the crank two complete revolutions very slowly, then remove the head.

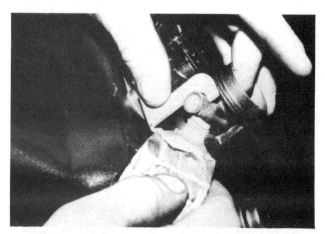

If the crankcase breather is not used, it should be plugged with silicone.

TDC set up.

Measure the thickness of the modeling clay and plastic. You must have at least .040" clearance between these moving parts.

Final Assembly

After trial assembly, completely disassemble the engine, marking parts such as lifters, rockers, pushrods, etc., to be sure that they go back in the same locations.

During final assembly of the engine, to properly install studs clean all threads until each stud can be screwed in and out with finger pressure only. Then use a chemical

This tool can easily be made with a socket to turn the crank.

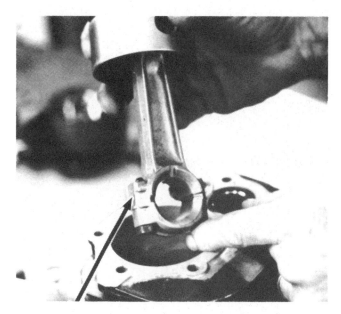

The tabs on the rod and cap must be placed next to each other to retain the factory alignment.

Correct installation of the slinger.

Proper installation of tin. Note the three longer head bolts are around the exhaust valve.

mix to all moving and rubbing surfaces, and all bearings, as the parts are put together.

If the engine will not be run in the immediate future, do your assembly using extreme pressure grease (not chassis lube) and rub it into each of those bearings and surfaces. Also, use a moly cam break in lube on cam surfaces, lifters, pushrod ends, and rocker pivots.

Chemically clean all parts one final time. Then lubricate with STP/oil mix, or EP grease and moly disulfide, and

cleaner such as Loctite solvent or brake cleaner spray, and allow the threads to dry completely. Put a small amount of red Loctite on the stud threads that will go into the basic part. Screw the stud in until it bottoms, then back it out 1/8th of a turn. Mount the part that will be attached by the studs, and tighten it in place (5-10 inch pounds). This will ensure that the stud is in proper alignment as the Loctite solidifies.

As the engine is assembled, decide about how soon it will be run. If it will be run within a few days, then use a 50-50 mix of STP and 30 wt. oil, and liberally apply that

Torquing the head. Take three passes, working your way up to 140 inch/pounds.

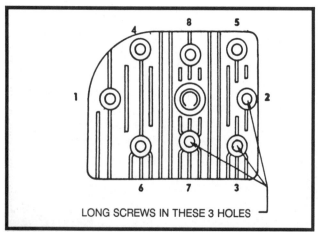

Head bolt torquing pattern.

The three holes near the exhaust valve take the longer head bolts.

Correct alignment of the two timing marks on the crank and cam gears.

Offset flywheel keys are available from kart shops. The flywheel can be installed without a key but a small amount of valve grinding compound should be smeared on the mating surfaces.

assemble. After each nut and bolt has been cleaned and inspected, apply a thin film of motor oil to the threads and install them with a good torque wrench.

If all of this seems like a lot of bother with a little engine, remember that if it is turning 6000 RPM, a 20 second lap will have subjected the parts to the pressures and heat of 1000 explosions, while each valve has been hammered open and closed a thousand times.

All of the parts used are very over stressed, so the faster the engine turns, and the more laps are put on it, the sooner something is going to wear out or break.

This is why experienced and knowledgeable racing engine builders go to extreme lengths to guarantee clean-

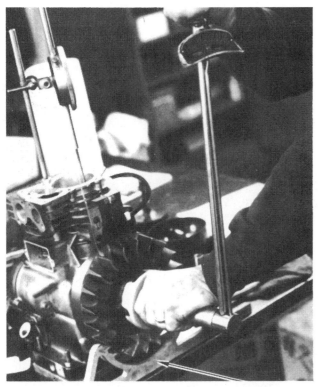

The flywheel is torqued to 70 ft/lbs on the Briggs. Note the flyweel holder (arrow). The holder and the special clutch wrench are made by Briggs & Stratton.

liness and perfect fit of parts. This is also why hiring a professional builder is cheaper in the long run, although he may appear expensive at first.

Valve Float

One of the terms that you will hear around any race track is "valve float". By this, most people are referring to the fact that at very high speeds, momentum causes a valve to continue to open, even though the cam should be allowing it to close. This is dealing with something that engineers call "valve bounce", which is a more descriptive term.

Experiments with strobe lights and ultra high speed movie cameras have shown that, in a running engine, valve springs are never standing still. Even when the valve is closed, and there is clearance between the lifter and the valve, a form of harmonic vibration causes the center coils of the spring to move up and down rapidly. Valve bounce occurs when the frequency of this vibration exactly matches the shock imposed when the valve closes against the seat. When this happens the valve will bounce open several times, in an uncontrolled fashion. Depending on which valve is involved, here are the things that will happen.

Intake: Since the piston will be rising on the compression stroke, some of the fuel/air mixture will be forced back into

This valve spring compressor is available from Briggs & Stratton.

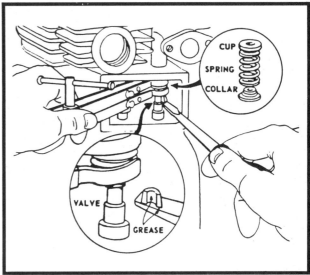

Removing the valve spring. (Drawing courtesy of Briggs & Stratton).

the intake valve pocket. This results in less power being produced.

Exhaust: Since this happens as the piston is going down on the intake stroke, there is less mixture drawn through the intake valve, and some exhaust gasses are drawn back through the exhaust valve. This results in a diluted mixture, and less power. Heavy-duty valve springs are designed to raise their frequency well above the impact frequency that the valves might experience. Shimming stock springs (at least .050" shims) will often help, but usually will not cure the problem completely. If you shim the springs, be sure that there is at least .060" clearance between the coils when the valve is completely open.

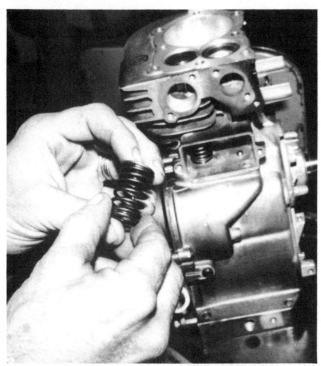

The valve springs on the Briggs are wound tighter at the top to reduce vibrations and retard valve float.

What most people hear, and call, "valve float", is a sudden flattening of the power curve as the engine abruptly slows its acceleration. This may be caused by ignition or valve timing, but is most often caused within the intake system. Actual valve bounce will reduce available power and acceleration, but the engine often will still accelerate, although at a slower rate.

Limitation of fuel flow at high RPM, causing a sudden, drastically lean mixture, might cause this flattening out. More often the cause is a shock wave created within the venturi system, which sends a "wrong signal" to the fuel mixture circuitry, or even actually chokes the air flow to the engine.

If you think your engine is experiencing "valve float" there is a simple test to be made. Put the rear end of the kart on supports, and run the engine at full throttle until the RPMs stabilize. If it still "floats" at the same RPM as it did while driving, your problem is in the valve springs or the cam. If the engine will run at higher RPMs without load, the problem is more likely somewhere in the intake system.

For example, an experimental kart engine was run on the test stand, without load, into the 11,000+ RPM range a number of times. On the track, under load, it peaked at 6700 RPM.

Despite the fact that the valves and springs had been proven satisfactory at as high as 11,300 RPM, several individuals commented that "I can hear the valves floating" at about 6500 RPM.

The problem was found to be in the needle valve area of the carburetor, which furnished enough fuel for "free running" at high RPM, but was not adequate for the demands of moving the weight of the kart and driver at the lower speeds.

By simply drilling the two small holes (see "Carb Fine Tuning") which supply fuel to the jet, the problem was corrected, and the engine regularly ran 7400-8000 RPM.

Piston and Rings

Many racing mechanics advocate using a .010" (.25mm) oversize top compression ring, with the proper sized second compression and oil control rings, filed to the correct end gap. Their reasoning is that this gives a greater pressure between the top ring and the cylinder wall, resulting in a better ring seal, and less ring flutter. Those who oppose this idea contend that the increased ring tension causes increased ring drag (friction) thus actually decreasing the total power of the engine. They also point out that a major responsibility of the top ring is to transfer heat from the piston dome to the cylinder wall, and that the increased ring tension causes additional heat that acts as a "heat block". For the Briggs, Richard Hearn uses a .010" oversize compression ring and files it to a .008" end gap. The second ring is set at .018" gap and the oil control ring uses .021" of gap.

Another idea that should be discussed has been around since the mid-30's, and has to do with piston installation. If a piston has a mark stamped on the top surface, is flat on the top, and the shop manual states that this mark should point in a certain direction when the piston is installed, that means that the wrist pin bore is off center in the piston. The purpose of offset wrist pins is to decrease the amount of piston slap (a tiny rocking motion of the piston as it moves up and down) when the engine is cold. Piston slap creates a knocking noise, and increases the rate of piston skirt wear. This rocking motion of the piston also requires power, which must be robbed from the engine.

Reversing the piston on installation, making the mark point the "wrong way", changes the connecting rod angle as the crankshaft nears top dead center. This results in an effect similar to the piston remaining at TDC longer than it would normally, allowing the combustion pressure to increase at the most critical point in the power stroke. The pistons on two-cycle engines cannot be turned around because the ring gap would protrude into the intake port and it would break. This little trick is one of those modifications that makes a small horsepower difference, perhaps 1/2 to 1% improvement in horsepower, but adding several of those little changes will create one of the best motors around.

Chapter 7

ENGINE BLUEPRINTING

In many classes of racing, an engine builder is allowed to "blueprint" the engine. This means to add, remove, and machine metal to bring each part of the engine to the manufacturer's ideal measurements that will combine with other measurements to get the maximum design power from the engine.

The reason for this lies in operating conditions on the manufacturer's design board, his production line and the intended use of the engine. Most parts are machined within certain tolerances, which for a street motor, or as in our case a stationary powerplant, are set quite liberally. While the parts that fall within the preset "plus or minus" are perfectly good for the purpose they were designed for, they could be improved by narrowing the allowable range of the dimensions or by machining the parts to one of the extremes of the tolerances allowed, depending on the role the part plays in the engine.

For example, a particular cylinder head may have a design thickness of .760." If you could get into a large warehouse and measure a hundred or more heads, you might find heads that range from .760" to as high as .795." Every other part that was machined in production will show similar ranges.

"Blueprinting" means to determine the ideal legal measurement for each part (the measurement that will produce the ideal action from that part) and then modify it as necessary to attain that "ideal." It is possible to get as much as a 20-25% power increase by just making the engine conform to the manufacturer's "ideal" specifications.

In many classes of racing blueprinting is not permitted. In these cases, the process known as "selective assembly" permits a similar and legal effect — although only a 5 to 8% power increase can be achieved. Here one must have access to a large supply of parts to choose from. By measuring the various parts, and selecting those which most nearly approach "ideal" measurements, noticeable power increases can be found. Note that this is completely legal under the rules of most racing organizations. No parts have been altered and no machining has been done. All that was done was to select the best parts that were available

from the manufacturer. Learning the codes that are cast, or stamped, on each part will often be of help too.

Camshafts

Probably the most important part of a racing engine, for producing power, is the camshaft. The millisecond differences in the timing of valve actions, and the changes that can be made by modifying or changing camshafts, have a great effect on the power and torque curve and its ultimate peak.

Depending on the rules of the organization and class, there are several things that can be done to realize considerable power increases. But first, it must be decided exactly how the engine will be used. Will it be run on short ovals? Mostly on fast tracks with long straights and sweeping turns? On tracks with long straights and some tight turns? Whatever type of track the engine will be raced on, if the rules permit modifying the camshaft, will require the help

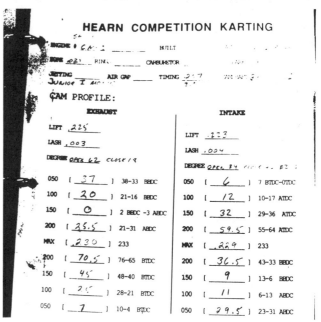

Camshaft spec sheet used by engine builders. A copy of this sheet should be provided with a motor when it is prepared by a professional engine builder.

Dial indicator and degree wheel are being used to check valve timing and cam profile.

Arrow points to the crankshaft gear key. The key must be perfectly straight before installing the gear. Any movement will change the cam timing.

of a cam grinder or an engine builder who deals with one. Give him a description of your engine, any modifications that you have done or plan on doing, the tracks that you expect to drive on, and ask for his advice.

If the rules require the use an unmodified stock cam, follow the selective assembly route (see "Blueprinting"). Often you can find another stock cam that will drastically outperform the cam that came with the engine.

Many compromises are made when a manufacturer designs an engine. Some will go on electric generators, requiring constant high speed with gradual variations in load (as power units are turned on or off), within a fairly tight overall range. This engine would use a camshaft designed to run in the upper horsepower range. Others of this basic engine will go on garden cultivators, subject to sudden heavy loads requiring maximum torque throughout the operating range.

Still others of these engines will be designated as general purpose, where the manufacturer cannot predict where and how they will be used. These GP (general purpose, not Grand Prix) engines will receive a camshaft that is a compromise grind. To do this, a manufacturer might cast cam blanks from several different molds, providing for different amounts of valve overlap (the time when the intake and exhaust valves are both open). They may then grind the individual lobes to several different profiles (shapes), giving

After applying a small amount of valve lapping compound to the flywheel taper, it is held against the spinning crankshaft. This helps the flywheel seat to the crankshaft and, if needed, allows the flywheel to be used without a key to set the ignition timing.

a total of as many as 20 different camshafts that all fit the same basic engine.

If you can gain the confidence of a dealer, who will let you study the brochures and parts catalogues for various applications of the basic engine, you can find the correct stock number for a camshaft that is designed for the performance desired.

It will take some time and energy to trace down the camshaft that is best for the unique engine, kart, track and technique combination. IKF and WKA now allow the use of reground cams in stock classes. Running a class that allows those cams would be a lot easier, if this is permitted by your local organization's Tech Specs.

Camshaft Testing

After selecting the cam, assemble the engine, break it in well, and drive enough to get accurate lap time averages. Preferably run at least 4 or 5 sets of 4-lap tests, and then average them.

Tear the engine down enough to remove the crankshaft. Mark the crank to show the exact position of the cam drive gear. Have the gear pressed off, move it 1/2 tooth clockwise, and press it back on. Reassemble the engine and test this combination as we described above. Then move the gear so that it is 1/2 tooth counterclockwise from the original, reassemble, and test this setup. Finally, decide which of the three cam timing setups gave the best average lap times. Reposition the drive gear (if necessary) and race the engine that way.

Keep in mind that advanced camshaft timing will move the power curve down to the lower RPM range. This would be more helpful on short tight tracks and speedway racing. Retarding the cam timing will shift the power curve up, causing power to be produced at higher RPM. This would improve lap times on a track with longer straights and sweeping curves, where top speed and aerodynamic resistance are important factors.

Cam Bushings and Wear

Most kart engines have aluminum crankcases and side plates, and the cam bearings are oiled by splash, compared to a pressurized automotive system which would maintain a film between the surfaces. With the combination of the soft crankcase and side plate material and the pressure of the valve springs, the cam pockets wear fairly rapidly. This allows extra play between the cam gear and the crank gear, resulting in a gradual change in the valve timing and increasing the impact loading on the gear teeth.

Both steel and aluminum gears will cause an eventual loss of power when these bushings wear and the aluminum gears, if they are allowed to wear enough, will shear the teeth. This wear problem is accelerated by competition camshafts. The wear can also make an engine illegal by changing the valve timing.

Two approaches can be taken to solve this problem, but both are rather expensive: 1) As a repair fix, find a good welder (FAA rated is best) who can build up the bearing

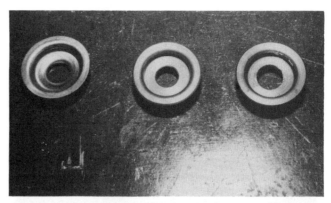

At left is a Briggs valve spring retainer, center is a Tecumseh upper retainer, and right is a Briggs. The upper retainers should be checked to ensure the valve stem passes through freely. The Briggs upper retainer is thicker than the Tecumseh, which may cause some bind when the part gets hot. The Briggs retainer is very hard and it cannot be drilled, so substituting the Tecumseh piece is a good idea, if rules permit.

areas of the crankcase and side plate without any warpage. 2) Have a machinist mill both bearing areas to accept a replacement bushing in exactly the original position. Of course if the bearing area is worn, it will need to be welded or bored out further to accept a larger bushing or bearing.

In either case, drill two small oil holes through the support area and the bushing in positions that will allow oil to run down and lubricate the bushing. A needle bearing may not need oiling holes and it will reduce friction, thus yielding some additional power. Purchase the bearings or bushings from an engine builder or a large bearing house such as King Bearing.

Boring

Sooner or later the cylinder will need to be rebored, the block decked, and cylinder head milled. A word of caution before we consider the subject, and before you give your parts to someone for alteration.

Find out exactly how the machinist makes certain that all machining is done at the proper angles. Even properly clamping a block onto a machine table does not guarantee that all the angles are in the correct relationship. Explain to the machinist all the relationships of the operation. For example, explain to him that the top of the cylinder must be at exactly 90 degrees to the rod and the bore of the cylinder, not just straight.

If a machinist gets impatient at the questions, or gives you a vague snow job, get yourself another man. You are paying good money for work that is the key to a good engine, and you deserve to get the best work available.

A dial indicator is used up and down in the bore to check for squareness. A tolerance of 0.002-inch maximum is used.

Boring head used to bore cylinders. These bars are quite expensive because they must be very stiff to prevent vibrations.

The motor is placed on two stands that are bolted to the mill table. A shaft is inserted through the crankshaft bearings. A stud and locknut is placed under one side of the motor.

A step block is inserted under the other side of the motor. Feeler gauges are added under the block until the deck is straight.

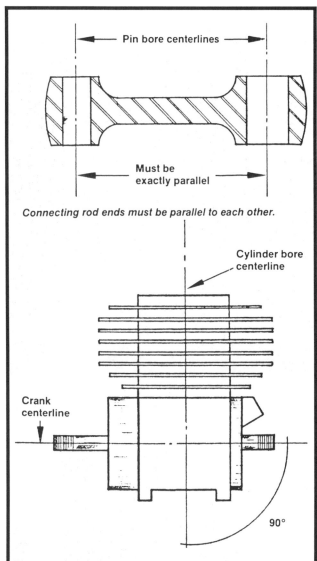

Connecting rod ends must be parallel to each other.

The cylinder base must be machined true to the crankcase so the crankshaft plane runs exactly perpendicular to the connecting rod.

Machining Guidelines

All the horizontal surfaces must be parallel to each other. The crankshaft, camshaft, block deck, wrist pin, cylinder base and top must be parallel and on the same plane to each other. The connecting rod, piston sides and cylinder bore must also be parallel to each other in addition to being perpendicular to the horizontal parts. If the cylinder and piston are to be taken to a machine shop that does not normally deal with race motors, it would be advisable to figure out the piston clearance desired and give it to the machinist.

Be sure the machinist knows that a hone is to be used for the final surfacing of the cylinder bore. The correct cross hatch pattern must be applied to achieve good ring seal

Cylinder hones can be purchased from K & P. A quick in and out motion is necessary to get the correct cross hatch pattern.

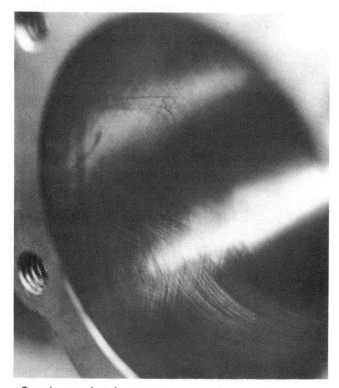

Good cross hatch pattern.

and quick seating. The correct pattern is much courser than what would be applied to a stock engine. A good tool to invest in is the cylinder hone kit part number T-3950, available from K&P Manufacturing. This tool will allow you to do your own hone jobs and it will pay for itself in a hurry.

It would probably be less costly to send the parts to an experienced kart engine builder than having a shop set up the jobs and make the tooling. For example, Hearn Com-

A small amount of valve lapping compound is placed on the crank bearing surfaces. A drill is then used to turn the crankshaft. This polishes the rubbing surfaces and reduces friction. The process is not used on the side using the bearing.

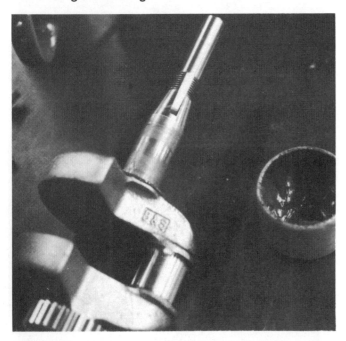

The crankshaft after it was lapped. The valve lapping compound must be washed off thoroughly as it is very abrasive and it will damage the engine very quickly.

petition Karting receives parts from all over North America with a simple explanation note and a follow up phone number in case a question comes up.

The head is being surfaced. Note shim material used to square it. Heads can also be sanded on a surface plate.

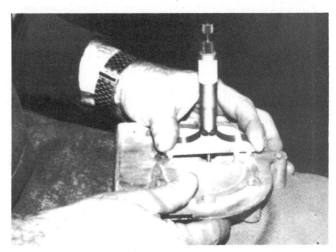

Rules require certain minimum depths on the head. The closer you can get to the minimum, the more compression the motor will have.

Milling

Before having any work done on the deck and/or head, assemble the engine, using old gaskets. Place strips of modeling clay, with plastic kitchen wrap on both sides, anywhere that you think the piston or valves will come close to something. Install the head and valve mechanism,

The head gasket is a tech item in stock classes. Minimum thickness allowed is 0.047-inch, and no sealers can be used.

torquing the head bolts or nuts to the normal reading. Turn the engine over, very carefully, for just two revolutions.

Remove the head, and measure each strip of clay and plastic. Remember that your connecting rod and valves get longer as they get hot, and tend to stretch slightly each time they suddenly reverse their direction of movement. This means that you must maintain at least .035" of clearance when the engine is running. This requires about .040" cold. Use a magic marker to mark the gasket surfaces of the head and block, and indicate the exact amount that needs to be removed to provide that .040" clearance. For example, if the clay measures .063", .023" could be removed.

Remember that the amount removed from the deck might affect what is removed from the head, and vice versa. And, never remove enough from the deck to let the top piston ring come any closer than .150" from the deck surface.

Finally, be sure that your machinist grinds these surfaces or mills them slowly with a fly cutter so the surface will be smooth enough to provide a good seal.

Valve Grinding

Many karters believe that any local auto shop will give them as good a valve grind as they need in a kart engine. However, much more work and care needs to be applied to a race motor. If rules permit, grinding the valves and seats at multiple angles will be of benefit. The following descriptions should be of value:

2-angle valve grind (valve) — grind the valve face to the usual 45-degree angle. Then undercut, using a 24-degree angle for the intake valve, and a 16-degree angle for the exhaust valve, leaving a surface of about the same width

Valve seat cutting tool being used on the intake seat.

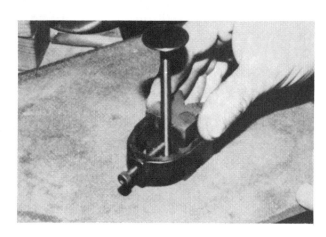

Method for changing valve length to alter valve timing.

as the valve face. This will offer a blended or curved effect between the valve stem and the seating surface.

2-angle grind (seat): use a good stone for the basic 45-degree grind on the seating surface. Then, with a 30-degree stone, narrow the seating surface to about 1/16." This provides a curved effect between the valve seat and the combustion chamber.

3 angle grind (seat): Grind the valve seat to about twice the width used for a 2-angle grind, using the 45-degree stone. Then with a 60-degree stone for the bottom cut, blend the seat into the port area. Finally, using the 30-degree stone, set the final seat width of 1/16-inch.

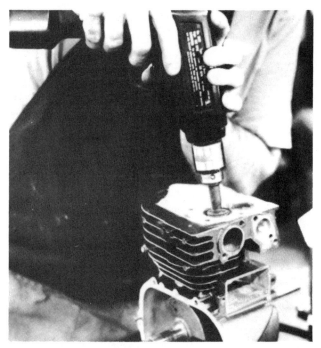

A small electric drill can be used with an automotive valve lapping cup to seat the valves after grinding.

The 5-angle grind (seat) is often called a "radius grind." This goes beyond the "3-angle" job. After completing the three grinds involved in the "3-angle", make final passes with a 15-degree stone in the combustion area, and a 75-degree stone in the valve port area. Then carefully remove all sharp edges except those on both sides of the 45-degree area.

Some people suggest grinding valves to an angle of 1 to 2 degrees more (or less) than that of the valve seat angle. Their rationale is that this gives a finer seating surface, and thus a tighter seal after the valve is closed.

While it is true that this will give a smaller seating area, it also gives much poorer transfer of heat from the valve head to the seat. This will then accelerate the erosion and burning of the valves but in a race engine the advantages outweigh the slight loss in reliability

Porting

Some classes allow more extensive modifications where grinding the intake and exhaust ports would be legal. This is done to improve the flow of air/fuel mixture from the carburetor into the combustion chamber, and the exhaust flow out of the engine.

Using a high speed grinder, shape and polish the valve pockets between the gasket surfaces and the valve seats. In the case of a 3 or 5-angle valve seat grind, stop the cuts at the bottom cut seat grinding location.

Work toward a smoothly changing cross sectional area. It requires some finesse to maintain the desired cross sectional area at each point in the passage. The best bet here is to use a "D" shape anywhere the port bends, with the flat part of the "D" at the inside of the bend. Include the valve guides in this activity, but remove as little of the guides as is absolutely necessary.

The object of porting is to improve both the quantity and the quality of the flow. Therefore, the smoother and more consistent the overall grind and polish, the greater the effect and the better the flow.

Making the port as huge as possible does not always equate to more horsepower. In fact, having the ports ground out to a cross sectional area larger than the area that is available when the valve is open (the cylindrical area between the valve and the seat) will result in flow stagnation, fuel drop out, and erratic combustion in the cylinder.

The amount that the ports should be enlarged depends on how you expect to use the engine. Generally, smaller ports are more power producing in the lower RPM range. The larger ports, with their greater volume while the valve is closed, will give more power in the higher RPM range (above 7000).

The best bet, if you usually run on tracks of less than 1/2-mile length, is smaller ports to get off the corners quicker, sacrificing a little peak power and speed between the middle of the straights and the next corner. A novice driver will be better off with smaller ports to compensate for his slower exit speeds or for when he gets stuck in traffic.

When you finish with the port grinding, place old valves in the guides to protect the seats and deburr and polish the combustion chamber. This will not only improve the flow of gasses in and out, but will help resist detonation and reduce carbon build up.

Care should be taken in grinding not to punch a hole through the port.

The objective in port grinding is to obtain the smoothest and greatest mixture flow in the RPM range the engine will be raced in. Smaller ports give better response off corners. Larger ports help more during the periods when you can run in the higher RPM range. For best results, you must consider the carburetor, the manifold and the cam, to decide how much to remove and where to remove it from. The actual contour should be shaped to obtain even flow all the way around the valve and the seat. The ports should narrow down as they approach the seat. This builds up velocity and reduces pressure at that point. Special care should be taken with the area one inch directly under the seat. That is where most of the power is gained.

Lightening and Balancing

Lightening the piston, rod, and crank, will improve the acceleration potential of the engine, and ease the loads on the rods and bearings. Balancing gives a smoother operating engine, less likely to vibrate something to a point of

The crankshaft rod and main bearing surfaces are polished with fine emery cloth.

failure. It also decreases some of the forces on the crank, and on the rod and main bearings. Balancing can also improve power since an unbalanced rotating mass needs energy to vibrate.

The most important benefit from balancing a kart engine is in the area of improved longevity for these highly stressed parts. Remember the engine will be turning 2 to 3 times the RPM the manufacturer designed it to accept. Vibrations and power losses increase at the square of the speed. This means the forces on the parts have been increased from 6 to 9 times!

Study the piston, rod, and crank very carefully. Decide what direction stresses (compression, tension, and friction) work on each part, and draw rough sketches with arrows showing the direction of each force and do the filing and grinding along those lines, not at any angle. This is very important as the slightest scratch mark will constitute a stress riser which can develop into a crack. File or grind away every sharp edge, nick, or scratch, without going so deep that you destroy the surface tension that forging or casting has created, which provides much of the strength of the part.

Keep a perfect right angle at the bottom of the piston skirt. It acts as an oil scraper. If a radius is placed here it will force more oil up past the piston and the oil ring will not be able to handle this excess. Then oil will be forced into the combustion area.

If there are unstressed sections of a part, you might be able to drill or grind material away in a manner that will lighten the part without making it weaker. Examples here could be the center flange of the connecting rod, the wrist pin bosses inside of the piston, and the underside of the piston dome. The minimum dome thickness of .150" must be retained. Remember to smooth out any stress risers (nicks and scratches) that you created while lightening these parts.

The final step in stress removal and lightening is to take extremely fine stones (either grinder or hand) and polish every area which has been lightened or ground. Once again, be certain that the direction of the stone movements are parallel to the stress arrows in your sketches.

The engine can only be balanced after all the grinding and lightening has been done. The reason for this is if any more metal is removed when grinding, the part will be out of balance again.

The balancer will want all of the appropriate parts, cleaned and in final fitted form, before he starts his calculations for balancing. He will need the piston, with wrist pin and retainers installed, rings, properly filed for end clearance, connecting rod, with bolts, lock washers, and the bearing if it is removable. The crankshaft, with timing gear installed, and the flywheel will also be needed.

The flywheel should be lightened by the balancing shop or the engine builder. Flywheels store a tremendous amount of energy at high RPM and any flaw can cause them to disintegrate at great danger to the drivers and spectators.

Finally, some balancers do all of their balancing at the RPM at which the unbalanced engine would vibrate the worst. Others will make a final test and adjustment at the RPM that you indicate will be the fastest you expect to turn the engine in racing.

Exhaust Pipes

The first, and most important, consideration is having the inside of the pipe, match the exhaust flange on the engine perfectly.

The easiest way to determine pipe length, and still be fairly close to the ideal, is to make the pipe longer than is expected will be needed. Then paint it with cheap spray paint. Now, run the kart at racing speeds until the paint blisters away, and cut the pipe off where the burned area ends. This method will give an average of the range through which the exhaust is used on the track.

The following formula can be used to calculate the optimum pipe length for a given RPM (CI is cubic inches of the motor and D is pipe diameter):

$$\frac{CI \times 1900}{D^2 \times RPM}$$

Bends should be kept at a minimum to allow the best flow possible. Any bends that are necessary should be made with a minimum radius of 3 times the diameter of the pipe. For example, a pipe 1/2-inch should not have a radius of less than 1.5 inches (.5-inch x 3 = 1.5 inches).

If you run on a tight track, you might find that an anti reversion pipe may be of help. The basic factor here is that an AR pipe does very little for high RPM (above 5000), but it helps noticeably in the 3500-4500 RPM range. This may be an advantage on tracks with tight turns that require a lot of torque to come off the turns fast and get the jump on the competition.

To build your own AR pipe, first make a flange with a 3/4-inch long pipe attached. Match these to the engine exhaust flange. Then make an expansion chamber, about 3 inches long and 1.5 inches inside diameter, and mount your flange and pipe so that the pipe protrudes 1/2-inch into the chamber. Finally, add the necessary exhaust pipe, paint and burn, cut it off, and install the protective fender washer.

Testing an AR pipe made in this manner, we found that it improved racing performance on a little (1200-foot) local track, but showed no improvement on a long track (1.2 miles).

If rules permit, the crankcase breather can be run to the exhaust pipe to aid engine lubrication. Weld a 1/4-inch brake line fitting into the exhaust pipe and connect it to the breather on the engine. The exhaust pulses will draw the oil fumes from the engine to improve lubrication by creating a flow of fumes throughout the inside of the engine.

If any straight pipe is under 8 inches in overall length, always block or plug the pipe as soon as the engine stops. This will keep cold air from hitting the hot exhaust valve. The rapid cooling of the red hot valve could cause it to crack.

The basic rule of thumb on pipe length is that longer pipes improve low RPM torque, and shorter pipes help power at high RPM.

The final step in building a pipe for a four cycle is to weld a 2-inch diameter fender washer to its end to prevent injury should someone hit the tip.

Engine Break-In

A break-in period is necessary for an engine to allow all the rubbing surfaces to mate without creating any hot spots. A good break in will also allow the rings to seat properly, allowing a better seal and yielding more power. The valves will also gain from a break in period as they will seat better and last longer.

Another area that benefits greatly from a break in is the rocker arm pivot point. This part handles tremendous pressures with limited lubrication and if it is not broken in properly it will fail prematurely.

A simple 2 hour break in program can make the difference between an engine that lasts several weeks, and one that provides suitable performance for a half to a full season.

With the new engine installed on the kart, fuel in the tank, and oil in the crankcase, remove the spark plug. Crank the engine slowly, then more rapidly, some 10 to 12 times. This will distribute oil to the rod and main bearings, and ensure that nothing is going to hang up when it starts.

Start the engine, adjust the carburetor for a smooth operation at about 1500 to 2000 RPM, and let it run for about 20 minutes. Check carefully for any unusual noises, temperature, or vibrations during this period. Allow the engine to cool for 15 to 20 minutes, checking for looseness in shrouds, carb, exhaust mounts, etc.

Restart the engine, readjust the carburetor, and run for 20 minutes more. During this period open the throttle rapidly to about 3/4 opening, and let it close immediately. Do this about every 30 seconds. This will cause cooling of the concentrated heat on the hot points. It also allows oil to be pumped up past the piston rings, and aids in their seating.

Drain the oil while it is hot and test it with a magnet and filter (see "Choosing an Oil"), and put in new oil. Then go out to the track.

At the track, allow the engine to warm up at fast idle, readjust the carb for normal running, and take it for a drive. Spend about 20 minutes driving at slow speeds, not exceeding 3000 RPM while lifting off the throttle as often as possible. Stop and allow 10 minutes of cooling.

The next step is when you begin to "feel out" your new engine. Take it out on the track, driving in the 2000 to 3000 RPM range. Once a lap floor the gas pedal as you come out of a turn, holding full throttle for about 4 to 5 seconds. Then drop back to the 2000 to 3000 RPM range for the remainder of the lap.

After about 20 minutes of these accelerate and cool off cycles, stop, drain the oil for later testing, and head for home.

At home, allow the engine to cool completely while you perform some of the following tests and adjustments: Check the oil with a magnet and filter. Remove the cooling shrouds and check for fuel or oil leaks. Check valve clearances and ignition timing to be certain they are exactly what they should be. Retorque every nut and bolt that you can reach without getting inside the motor. Check chain adjustment and sprocket alignment. Reinstall cooling shrouds. Install new spark plug and refill crankcase with racing oil.

This program is basically simple. It allows the engine to be worked up to maximum stress and pressures, while a series of cool-off periods prevent the excessive localized temperature build-ups that could cause early failures during racing. Also, it gives a number of opportunities to check for leakage, noises, particles in the oil, etc., and to catch and correct any problems before they do damage.

Chapter 8

FINE TUNING TIPS

Aerodynamics

Many karters install various fairings, airfoils, and other aerodynamic devices, in an attempt to improve performance. A degree in aeronautical engineering is not needed to determine which devices will help and which are just money spent on looks.

Look at dragsters, Indy cars, and other vehicles that use these devices. In every case where wings are attached to the vehicle, they are raised as high as is permitted or practical. This is to get them into "clean" air, outside the turbulence that lies behind any object that is moving through the air.

Spoilers, such as seen on Winston Cup stock cars, are quite small, but used judiciously they still trim the handling because of their position and because the cars travel so fast. Comparing the size of the wings that you see on Indy and Formula I cars (moving in the vicinity of 200 mph) and sprinters and midgets (moving in the 80-120 mph range), you can see what it would take to have an effective wing on a kart.

At the slower cornering speeds of a kart, an effective wing would not only need to be mounted above the driver, in completely clean air, but it would need to be very large. In an enduro kart, a tail cone would be valuable. However, in a sprint or speedway kart, the disturbed air would make a cone ineffective. Wings on karts are generally a nuisance and are totally non functional.

Aerodynamically speaking, always keep in mind that in a tail cone the height to length ratio should be at least 3 to 1. This means that 3 feet of length are needed for each foot of height or width.

The front view of a kart with driver will show another story. Wheels, feet, body, elbows, knees, helmet, engine, steering wheel all contribute to the overall effects of disturbed air. The end result is somewhat like forcing a paddle through water, flat side first.

Aerodynamic devices, especially crude ones, are a compromise between drag and downforce. This side panel has doubtful effect on side force, while it is probably an anchor down the straights.

This clearly shows how much drag is caused by such things as cables, feet, arms, etc. Cleaning up that air stream is more beneficial than wings. The fairing helps deflect the air from the driver.

Fairings come in many shapes and they fit all kart chassis.

Noses, number plates and side fairings can be made out of old plastic pails.

Some parts and adjustments to the kart will help even in the 40 to 60 mile per hour range. A nose fairing that moves air smoothly past the wheels and driver's feet will reduce turbulence between the driver's legs, and an upper fairing will reduce turbulence in the steering wheel area. Another fairing on both sides of the kart will ease the air past the rear wheels and the engine. Tilting the seat back some without changing the desired weight distribution will reduce the frontal area. The greatest concern here is to clean up the air rather than reduce the frontal area. Items such as loose clothing and number plates, wings, high steering wheels, knees protruding out to the sides all contribute not only to the frontal area, but also to the quality of the air flowing around the kart. Remember that

These side pods assist the aerodynamics and they keep the other karts' tires out of the way where they could become entangled with yours.

one larger object will offer less resistance than several smaller objects of equal total size would.

There is no practical way to eliminate the disturbed air behind the kart. However that disturbance can be taken advantage of by another kart by utilizing the drafting technique. Study the Winston Cup or Indy car driver's technique on TV. On long straights one driver pulls up to a foot, or less, behind the other driver's rear bumper. The lead driver not only pulls the tailgater along, but he will often let him use the "slingshot" to pass him going into the next corner. The reason the first driver lets the towed car tag along is that this also helps the first car by creating a "freight train" vacuum effect which also cuts down on air drag for the first car.

Twin Engines

On the surface running two engines would seem to promise doubled power, with a minor weight increase. However, some have found that even with two engines, a good single engined kart would pull away from them. Others have found that at best the double power only meant a 4 to 5% decrease in lap times.

Think of a horse drawn vehicle, pulled by a Clydesdale and a Shetland pony. Obviously, the pony would just trot along, while the Clydesdale does all of the work. Even with two apparently matched horses, the stronger would work much more than the weaker.

The same concept applies to "hitching" two apparently identical engines together. Manufacturing or rebuilding tolerances (see "Blueprinting") will result in the two engines developing noticeably different power outputs.

Tests with engines geared together have shown that two apparently identical stock engines are a long ways from

Twin engine karts are fun, but they are more work. Twice the power, three times the work.

giving doubled power at the output shaft (axle, on a kart). The average comes to about 10 to 15% more horsepower, which converts to 3 to 4% reduced lap times.

However, all is not lost. It will take a lot of time, and a fair amount of money, but you can get two engines to within 90 to 95% of each other. Since speed varies with the cube root of horsepower at the wheels, you can get as much as a theoretical 15% decrease in lap time — if everything is perfect.

Start by blueprinting both engines. Then juggle the intake systems and exhaust systems to be sure that the fuel/air and exhaust gases flow in and out of both engines at exactly the same pressures and volumes.

Adjust ignition timing so that they are exactly alike (within 0 degrees), and rebuild the carburetors to assure that every hole, every passage, the needle valves and seats, float weights, and float levels match (measure them).

A final test you can make before installing the engines is for internal resistance — the power that it takes just to keep the engine running. Ideally, the resistance developed internally should be exactly the same. Although this is an impossibility, you will want to get as near to matching, in all respects, as you can.

This resistance comes from many areas, in 4-cycle, 2-cycle, diesel, and all other engines. These areas include:

1) Piston rings and skirts sliding against the cylinder wall.

2) Wrist pins sliding in the piston bosses and rod ends.

3) Crankshafts sliding against rod and main bearings and the seals.

4) Timing gear teeth sliding as they engage and disengage.

5) Valve springs being compressed, friction of the valve stems in the guides, pushrods, lifters and rockers.

6) The force it takes to move the gases in and out of the combustion chamber and to compress them.

7) Ignition systems.

8) Oil and air drag in the crankcase.

9) Vibrations.

When the engines have been fully assembled, with oil in the crankcase, but before they are installed on the kart, test them for balance as to the power needed to simply get them to rotate. Use an inch/pound torque wrench, and proceed as follows: Using the torque wrench on the flywheel nut, very carefully apply pressure (watching the torque reading) until the flywheel begins to move. Write down the torque reading that you saw at the point where friction was overcome. Repeat this trial and recording every 45 degrees of rotation until you have completed four revolutions with a four cycle and two rotations with a two cycle.

Make the same series of tests and recordings for the other engine. You can now make an informed comparison of the two engines. If the torque required for rotation varies between them, at any point in the cycle, this indicates a variation in the power that it will take just to keep each engine running — at that point — without it doing any actual work.

A little analysis of the factors and situation within the engine, at each point of testing, will give you an idea of what needs to be done to correct this imbalance.

Any variations, in any of the areas mentioned so far, will result in a "strong horse - weak horse" situation on a kart. Remember also that these readings were taken at speeds far below idle. Imagine what they would be when the engine gets hot, running fast, and the compression is developed by a rapidly moving piston!

Now is the time to disassemble the worst engine, if necessary, and try to reduce friction in the areas that you decide are causing the imbalance. Then reassemble, and retest, just to be sure. Finally, install the two engines on the kart, and match their installations as follows;

1) Be sure that the clutch and axle gears are in perfect alignment, and that the two chains are clean, lubricated, and adjusted to have the same tension.

2) Adjust your foot throttle cables so that each butterfly reaches the wide open position at exactly the same time.

3) Break in the engines as indicated in "Engine Break-in."

After you have broken in the engines, recheck the full throttle butterfly positions, and make final adjustments to the idle mixtures and speeds as follows:

1) Warm up the engines, and adjust the mixture needles to the highest RPM possible when idling.

2) Using an air mass gauge (Unisyn, or similar), set the idle speed so that each carburetor is drawing the same amount of air as the other.

3) With the air mass gauge removed, reset the mixtures for high RPM.

4) Test to see if the air mass requirements have changed. Adjust for balance if necessary.

5) Continue to alternate, setting mixture and air usage, until each engine is burning the same amount of fuel and air.

It is a lot of work, taking time and money, but you can install two engines and have them work together, not just impress spectators as being pretty. The question is whether the eventual performance is worth it. Do not expect a 100% increase in available power. Actually you will probably get a maximum of 70 to 80% more power at the wheels, which converts to about an 18% increase in top speed (remember, speed varies as the cube root of the power), and about 10% increase in rate of acceleration.

Total improvement in lap times or lap speeds will probably be in the vicinity of 12 to 15%, if everything is as perfect as you can get it.

Incidentally, be sure that your two clutches are adjusted so that they both start to slip at the same RPM, and both make the final "grip" at the same time see "Use Your Tachometer" section.

Speed and Power

One of the major misunderstandings for the newcomer to racing is the idea that doubling the power in an engine should double the speed of the kart. Unfortunately, it just does not work that way. As we increase the speed of our kart, we also increase the resistance to that speed. Friction increases fairly linearly with the speed. It takes more power to flex the chain, spin the wheel bearings, flex the tires, overcome increased tire scrubbing, and most importantly the aerodynamic resistance increases at the square of the speed. This means that to double your speed you need four times the available power! The result is that we have far less than a speed increase than is proportionate to the available power.

To reverse the equation, if the power is doubled it will increase the speed by the cube root of 2. Thus a 50% power increase will result in about a 14% improvement in performance, and a 100% increase in horsepower will give about 21% faster speed, or quicker lap times.

As a practical example, a "Bobcat" kart chassis was equipped with a stock Honda G-200 engine. According to the factory charts, this engine produces about 6 hp at 6000 RPM - with the governor removed. Later the engine was modified to "Super Stock" configuration, and still later to "Modified" or "Stock Appearing" status. Corresponding horsepower figures were computed by theoretical formulas and by comparison of foot-pound/second performance. These calculations agreed within 2.5% actual performance on a local 700' "sprint" track was as follows:

Engine	Fast Lap	HP Required
Stock	15.01 sec.	6.0
Super Stock	13.92 sec.	7.4
Modified	12.84 sec.	9.2

This shows that a 23% increase in horsepower just gave a 7.8% improvement in lap time, and a 53% horsepower increase only improved times by 16.9%.

Miscellaneous Tips

Remember a kart has no seat belts or rollbars — so when a kart driver flips, he does a lot of sliding!!! You can get a nice looking helmet for about $25 to $30, but it's degree of protection is questionable. The first time that you see someone sailing head first into a fencepost or barrier, you'll realize that the latest Snell approved models are well worth the price. Purchasing a helmet from a company which specializes in safety equipment is good insurance against getting a poor helmet.

Plastic and other good looking jackets and pants usually give little resistance to being torn — and your skin is right under them. Get the most abrasive-resistant material that can be found.

Also, the high priced professional racing gloves look very good, but are designed for protection against fire. Motocross or work gloves, made of leather, with heavy padding will protect the wearer against shock and abrasion much better than "Nomex" gloves will.

When racing at night or in cool weather with a neck support, the face shield on the helmet might start to fog up. Drill 4 to 6 1/8-inch holes along the bottom of the visor, just above the lower lip of the helmet window opening. These small holes will let air in, but keep debris out of the eyes and teeth.

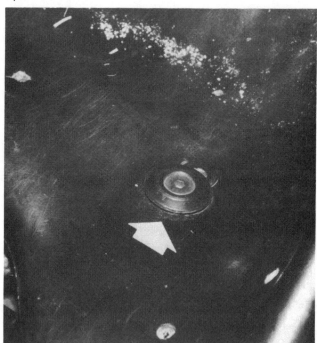

These large washers keep fiberglass seats from cracking around mounting bolts.

Using two bolts at the top of the seat mounts helps prevent the mount from cracking near the base where it clamps to the chassis.

For a custom fit in the driver's seat, use a spray-on foam insulation found in hardware or lumber stores. Lay a plastic trash can bag on the seat and sit in it. Spray the foam in the bag, making sure it is evenly dispersed and wait for the stuff to harden. When the foam cures, the plastic can be removed and you will have a permanent pad that can be left in the seat or removed if another driver wants to drive the same kart.

Safety wiring the axle circlip is a good idea. Should the hub come loose, the safety wire will keep the clip in place.

Use spring clips instead of cotter pins or safety wire, for any bolts that might need frequent removal for quick adjustment, such as on spindle nuts.

Safety wire, cotter pin, or spring clip all critical bolts. These devices, especially lock washers, are only designed to prevent the fastener from coming completely undone, only after it has come loose. Use lock nuts, Loctite or

These hair pin clips are very handy. Note the Spool wheels from K & P. These wheels are very light and they contain their own bearings.

Number plate holders can be made of angle iron or aluminum.

This caliper is properly mounted. It has safety wire across the fittings in case the mounting bolts come loose and allow the shims to slip out. The cotter pins at the end of the bolts are close to the self locking nuts to prevent them from backing out should they come loose.

double nut on any fastener that is critical such as engine mounts, seats, steering etc.

Vinyl house siding makes great material for number plates, dirt shields, cooling deflectors, etc. See a local building contractor for old pieces that you can get for free. Plastic pails also make neat body panels and number plates.

Clear Lexan 1/8" thick makes good covers for number plates, protecting your fancy numbers from another guy's tires.

A baby's ear syringe makes a handy tool for blowing dirt away from a spark plug before removing it, priming the carburetor, etc.

White contact paper from K-Mart can be painted any color that you want, for fancy decorations, numbers, etc. Their patterned paper gives you even more opportunities to be creative.

To make your steering wheel bigger and easier to grip, wrap it with clothesline, and cover with electrician's plastic tape. The irregular surface of the clothesline, and the plastic tape, combine to give a texture that is easy to grip, yet not sticky or sensitive to dirt.

Paint the ballast, exhaust pipes and mufflers with colors that contrast with the racing surface you'll be racing on. This way, if something falls off, it will be easier for everyone to see and avoid it. It would also be a good idea to have your name and/or number on those parts so they can be

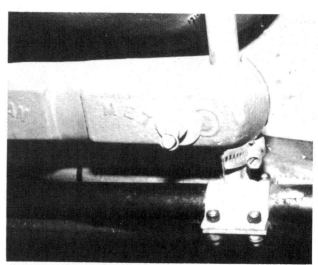

Good installation of this lead ballast. A lock nut is used along with safety wire and a large washer under the nut.

returned to you. Any part of the exhaust becomes obvious when it falls off, but ballast sometimes gets overlooked.

During the first one or two laps of tire warm-up or practice, drive at about half the speed that you usually would drive. This will let the piston, pin, rings, bearings, etc., get near to normal temp and lubrication before you put a heavy load on the engine.

After each race, or other high speed period, drive a lap or two at the same reduced speed. This will let the engine cool off evenly, and extend the longevity of the engine.

If you are not getting the power that you should get, there are many power robing areas in race motors. Start by checking the following:

1) Air cleaner, too small or dirty.
2) Carb passages and jets.
3) Low oil.
4) Fouled plug.
5) Loose wires.
6) Exhaust, clogged or dented.
7) Chain, dry or tight.
8) Throttle butterfly alignment and full opening.
9) Dragging brakes.
10) Worn or misaligned wheel bearings.
11) Air leak in the fuel line.

A 2" concrete chisel with rounded off edges can be used for such tasks as loosening tire beads, moving axle hubs (sprockets or brakes), etc.

If you use a do-it-yourself car wash to clean your kart remember that the high pressure water spray can take all of the grease out of a wheel bearing in just a few second. Kart shops sell plastic washers to protect the front wheel bearings. The tie rod spherical ends should also be protected from the steam.

Bumpers can be loosened or tightened to alter handling. The smoother the track, the more rigid the chassis should

Lots of do's and dont's are shown here. (1) The triangular brace on the seat strut would not be necessary if two botls were used at the top in the seat mount, and if the brace was bolted with all four bolts at the frame. (2) The bolts on this caliper should use lock nuts. If the nuts back off, the shim plates between the caliper halves will fall off. The cotter pins will stop the nut after it is too late. (3) A spring or safety wire should be used across the bleeder screws to prevent the shims from falling out. (4) Note the weld spot on the brake rotor key. Without that spot the key could come loose and slip out from under the rotor hub. This would cause the rotor to stop on the brake pads without stopping the kart. (5) The shimming material under the flangette bolts is used to align the bearing to reduce drag. (6) Note the broken brake line.

A catch can is easily made of any lightweight container. Plastic seems to work best.

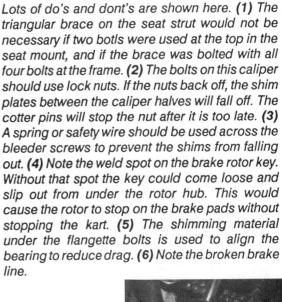

These pieces of shimming material are used to space the two flangette halves to allow the bearing and the axle to move around. This prevents the bearing and the axle from binding.

Arrow points to a triangulating bracket which helps prevent flexing of the bearing mount and the axle.

Bumper tabs prevent the bumpers from coming loose. They are good insurance.

be. The rougher the track, the more flex will be needed. A dirt track frame needs to be more flexible than an asphalt one. The heavier the class raced in, the stiffer the frame needs to be.

Nerf bars can also be used to control chassis stiffness. At least one end of each bar should have some play in it to prevent the bars or the mounts from cracking.

A flush-broken capscrew or stud can be removed by using a high speed grinder. Use a thin disc, and grind a slot across the broken area to allow the use of a screwdriver to remove the broken stud. Spraying the broken part with Pennzoil's Penz Guard will facilitate the task.

For a quick and accurate way of installing the proper amount of oil in an engine, park your kart on a perfectly level spot, and fill the crankcase to exactly the desired level. Drain this oil into a Ratio Rite, which can be purchased from most kart shops or use a household measuring cup. Note the amount of oil in the measuring cup and save it for future use.

When using dual fuel pumps, always connect them in parallel. Merge the outputs with an emissions control "Y" fitting to reduce pressure drop.

Semi metallic brake linings are far superior to standard linings. Remember to warm them up with a couple of medium applications during hot laps before each heat.

An old rule of racing says that if you drive an entire lap without lifting from the throttle, you can use more power. But if you have to lift anywhere, work on handling.

On many kart engines the fan blades cause so much turbulence at high RPM that blade stall occurs. If rules permit, cutting off every second or third blade can reduce head temp as much as 30 degrees.

If the front bumper or wheel hits the back of another kart's rear wheel at speed, you'll take a bicycle ride on the rear wheels. If you don't hit anything during this ride, you'll be ok. But if one of your rear wheels or the short nerf bar

commonly used for sprint racing climbs the other guy's wheel, you will probably flip. There is an easy solution that doesn't cost very much. Buy side nerf bars like midgets and sprint cars use from a kart manufacturer who offers them. Have them adapted to your chassis, with the front ends just inside the inner edge of the front wheels, and the rear ends about an inch ahead of your rear tires, and an inch inside the outer edges of those tires.

Also, the front number plate should be mounted vertically, as low as is practical, on the front side of the front bumper. This way, where the bumper might climb another driver's rear wheel, the flat number plate will just rub on his tire. Use carriage bolts for mounting so that you don't tear big chunks out of any tires that you might bump into.

Build a work stand, using 2 x 4s and 2 x 6s, that holds your kart just about waist level. Make it rigid enough so that you can run the engine, loosen or tighten bolts, etc., while the kart is at this convenient working level. If you put wheels on one end, and handles on the other, you can move it around without problems.

Inspect the bottom of the kart after every race meet. Pay particular attention to the welds on the crossbars under the seat. Remember, with no springs a kart flexes at the worst possible location — where the weight of the driver and engine is concentrated.

Rule Interpretation

The rule book should be studied and questioned if something is not perfectly clear. The rules written by the IKF and WKA are quite clear to the experienced racer but to the novice they may seem complicated. Smaller association rules may be very ambiguous.

Experience has shown that few people can write a set of rules that ten other people would all interpret as meaning exactly the same thing. The fact that the wording was clear to the writer or writers does not assure that everyone else will get the same meaning. Also, some rules are written by a group of racers who have gotten together with a thought in mind for a particular rule. While the way they wrote the rule makes sense to them because they had a definite reason for making that rule, the rule may mean something altogether different to a newcomer. It's your money that you are spending, and you cannot race successfully unless you know where you stand.

Examples of confusing rules were very evident when the rule books for a national and three local karting organizations were studied. Three of the four specified that in "stock" 4 strokes no metal could be removed from the block, head, valves, etc. Yet each one went on to authorize re-boring, grinding valves, valve seats, valve stems, and Helicoiling as needed. Each of these actions requires the removal of metal.

Note the heavy chain guard on this motor. The fins indicate that the guard was not always there. The spark plug wire is well protected with fiberglass sleeving and plastic wrap.

Chain guards are a must on all karts. If the chain breaks, the guard will keep it from flying away and possibly injuring someone. Chains can cause severe injuries such as broken arms and shoulders.

In addition to the "no metal removal" rule, one book stated that the head gasket surface may be blueprinted in "stock" and another states that the "cam must remain stock other than the lifter surface". Both state that gasket surfaces "may be remachined". Do these variations permit machining to the point of blueprinting?

Discuss any questions with the association president, tech inspection supervisor, race director, promoter, or whoever is in charge. Bring two or three witnesses with you, and hold out for definite answers that you can use to be sure that you will not be disqualified later, when he has forgotten a statement that you acted upon.

Talk to the other drivers and find out who actually makes the decisions (regardless of what the book says) and how consistently the rules are applied to everyone.

The Care and Feeding of Chains

Probably the most neglected item in kart maintenance is the drive chain. The chain is a simple item that should run for a long time, so long as you give it an occasional spray of oil. Yet if one is studied for a minute or two, it will become plain to see why things are not that simple and easy. First, each chain has quite a number of steel pins that are rubbing inside of steel tubes. These are commonly called "rollers", but it is obvious that there is no way that they can "roll." They just rub back and forth, at very high speeds, under considerable load, pressure, and heat.

Spraying oil (even chain lube) directly on these "rollers" does very little good. Time must be allowed for the lubricant to penetrate between each pin and the corresponding tube. Also, to keep the lube there under high centrifugal forces, always use a lubricant that goes in as a liquid, then condenses into a grease-like status such as the NEO spray from Baker Precision. The chain should be lubed after each heat. The lube must go along the side links on each side of the chain, then allow 8 to 10 minutes for penetration and evaporation before starting the engine so the centrifugal force will not sling the lube away. The clutch and axle gears should align so that the sprockets do not rub against the side links. Rubbing wears the gears and absorbs horsepower. The engine can shift a little on its mounts when you adjust chain tension, and the axle sprocket that you installed might align slightly differently than the one that it replaced.

Throw away the master link that comes with a new chain, and use a new link to make the connection solid and permanent. A bicycle chain breaker costs $4 to $5, and it will do a good job, although the $20 to $30 motorcycle or kart chain busters are much more convenient. Adjust the chain for a total (up plus down) of 1/2" slack at the middle of the upper part of the chain.

The chain should be replaced when it dries out more than is normal during a heat race, or when it has jumped off the sprocket. Measure its overall length (it was measured when it was new, was it not?), and replace it if it has stretched more than 1/4-inch. Be sure to carry at least one spare pre-lubed chain with you at all times.

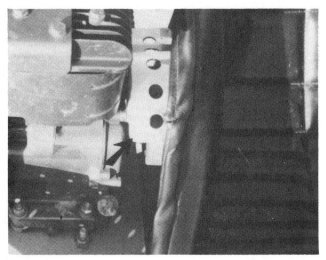

Chain guards are even more important on motors that use a power take-off on the inside of the kart near the driver's arm.

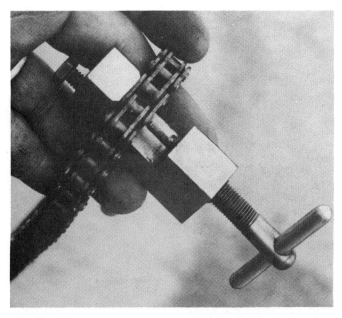

These small chain breakers should be in every karter's toolbox. They can be purchased from most kart shops.

Any time the chain jumps off the sprocket it means that two things have happened:

1) There has been an installation error (too much slack, sprockets misaligned, or both), and

2) The chain has had to stretch in order to get up and over the sprocket teeth.

Another commonly overlooked reason that causes the drive chain to jump off is a weak or overly flexible frame.

The gear hub should be checked to ensure its straightness. It could cause the chain to jump off if it is not true.

For motors with the power take off facing the outside of the kart, it is important to keep the tire at least an inch away from the gear. The tire will flex under as it is loaded in a turn and it will put pressure on the gear, causing it to bend. Too large a gear can contact the ground in a turn and cause the chain to jump off.

To obtain the absolute minimum power loss in a chain, it should be removed after every race meet and checked for stretch. It should be washed very carefully, allowed to dry then put in boiling transmission lube, and then set aside to cool. Reinstall it, then lube it normally after each heat.

If you want your chain to last as long as possible, here is an old trick that worked back in the days of chain driven dirt track racers: Remove the chain after each race meet, inspect, and replace it if necessary. Wash it carefully in solvent, hang it up for at least two hours to dry completely inside the "rollers."

Coil the chain in a coffee can, put in a handful of high temperature wheel bearing grease, and heat slowly until the grease is completely melted. Allow a couple of hours for the grease to congeal inside of the "rollers". Remove the chain, wipe off the excess grease, and reinstall it on the kart.

Regardless of whether your organization rules require it, always have a good clutch and chain guard on your kart. Design it so that a broken chain cannot fly up and hit the driver, or fly back and hit the guy behind in the face.

SUPPLIER'S DIRECTORY

Publications

The Inside Track
P. O. Box 601
Vinton, IA 52349
(319) 472-4763

National Karting News
51535 Bittersweet Rd
Granger, IN 46530
(219) 277-0033

Associations

International Karting Federation (IKF)
4650 Arrow Hwy., C7
Montclair, CA 91763
(909) 625-5497

World Karting Association (WKA)
5725-D Hwy 29 North
Harrisburg, NC 28075
(704) 455-1606

Suppliers

American Power Sports
12300 Kinsman Rd.
Newbury, OH 44065
(216) 564-8100

Briggs & Stratton
Motorsports Division
P.O. Box 702
Milwaukee, WI 53201
(414) 259-5333
(800) 276-0765

Jim Hall Kart Racing School
1555-G Morse Ave.
Ventura, CA 93003
(805) 654-1329

Hearn Competition Karting
125 E. Santa Clara, #6
Arcadia, CA 91006
(818) 574-0890

Horstman Manufacturing
2510 Pioneer Ave.
Vista, CA 92083
(760) 598-2100

K & P Manufacturing
950 W. Foothill
Azusa, CA 91702
(818) 334-0334

Kart World
1488 Mentor Ave.
Painesville, OH 44077
(216) 357-5569

Kinney Motorsports
496 E. St. Charles Rd.
Carol Stream, IL 60188
(630) 668-9400

Pitts Performance
7922 Woodley Ave.
Van Nuys, CA 91406
(818) 780-2184

Simpson Race Products
2415 Amsler Ave.
Torrance, CA 90505
(310) 320-7231
(800) 654-7223

T.S. Racing
123-C W. Seminole Ave.
Bushnell, FL 33513
(352) 793-9600

Target Distributing
19819 Orchard St.
South Bend, IN 46637
(800) 348-5076